HEALING WITH RADIO

The natural self-healing powers of the body can be blocked by stress and negative emotions. Radionic therapy is regarded as a potent method for removing such blockages and for stimulating the flow of healing forces.

HEALING WITH RADIONICS

The Science of Healing Energy

by
A. L. G. DOWER

THORSONS PUBLISHING GROUP

First published 1980
Second Impression 1981
This revised edition 1988

British Library Cataloguing in Publication Data

Dower, A. L. G.
Healing with radionics: the science of
healing energy. — 2nd ed.
1. Radiesthesia
I. Title
615.8'5   RZ600

ISBN 0-7225-1541-3

*Published by Thorsons Publishers Limited, Denington Estate,
Wellingborough, Northants, NN8 2RQ, England*

Printed in Great Britain by Woolnough Bookbinding Limited,
Irthlingborough, Northants

10 9 8 7 6 5 4 3 2

Contents

To the memory of Malcolm Rae

Foreword

The form of therapy of which this book is a most competent exposition has been written up by other writers, such as Edward Russell in his excellent *Report on Radionics*, but the outstanding merit of the present book by Lavender Dower is that she is and has been an actual radionic practitioner who has followed the fortunes of this new therapy from the 1950s to the present, and has taken part in its development, growth and expansion. She knows, having borne 'the heat and burden of the day', what she is talking about from her first-hand work and experience.

The author has also had the great good fortune to have collaborated with the late Malcolm Rae. Under his masterly guidance she has had the opportunity to try out and use his inspired ideas and concepts in the treatment of patients. It is thus fitting that the book should be dedicated to him, as his prolific genius has contributed so much which is now fundamental to this whole supersensible medical dimension—more especially its radionic aspect.

A definition of radionics is that it is instrumental radiesthesia, a variant of medical dowsing in which no, or very few, instruments are required. The common and essential factor linking the two is, of course, the radiesthetic faculty—that supersensible sense without which it would be impossible to explore or treat a patient's etheric or life body (or that of a plant or animal) which is the working realm of both radionic and psionic medicine.

As far as orthodox medicine is concerned there should be no antagonism or rivalry as their spheres and roles are different. Radionics is, in fact, not an alternative but a very necessary and vital ally and complement, hitherto unrecognized. This is illustrated and authenticated in the later chapters of the book, which include pedology, agronomy, agriculture and veterinary science.

If this could be appreciated and recognized, a real breakthrough in the art and science of healing would result. This is the reason I recommend this book wholeheartedly to all who are seeking the all-embracing, holistic medicine of the future.

Aubrey T. Westlake B.A., M.B., B.Chir.,
M.R.C.S., L.R.C.P.
F.I.Psi.Med.,
Hon.F.Rad.A.

Introduction

Leonardo da Vinci, whose thinking was way ahead of his own time, once said: 'Nature never breaks her own laws'. It is upon this truism that the science of radionics is based.

The fundamental law of cause and effect is something which concerns the radionic practitioner above everything in his work of healing the sick. It is of little value to deal with the effect of illness without first discovering the cause; indeed, the suppression of symptoms may lead to a far more serious condition, even if the sufferer gains temporary relief.

Nothing ever happens without a cause and a radionic analysis is like a true life detective story, taking the patient as a whole, on all levels, spirit, mind and body and tracing the threads of his symptoms back to their origin.

The science of radionics is the detection and identification of the myriad different energy patterns which are emitted by all forms of matter, patterns which can be distorted and thrown into disharmony by psychological states, viruses, bacterial influences and injuries.

The aim of radionic therapy is to remove or reverse the original causes of the patient's illness. This, however, cannot be done without the co-operation of the patient as it is always the patient who heals himself in the end.

Radionics may guide the patient's inner being to bring about a recovery: it may remove blockages and open up the channels for the life force to flow freely. It may even influence the consciousness of cell formations in the patient's body but it is the patient's own life force which will perfect the healing.

If we are to understand radionic therapy it seems we must accept that force fields surround all matter and that every human, animal, insect, plant, bacterium, hormone and mineral has its own corresponding force field energy pattern. Whether we truly understand what these energy fields consist of is another question. However, the fact that force fields of some kind do exist is now quite widely accepted.

More fundamentally, it seems that we must also assume a rhythm which permeates all life and which stems from the source of all energy, cosmic consciousness, or whatever words you may wish to describe it. It is when this rhythm is interrupted or gets out of tune, that disharmony and illness emerge. This disharmony is reflected in an altered energy pattern.

Further, it seems there must be a non-physical as well as a physical dimension to radionic therapy. Thought may be regarded as essentially non-physical in nature and it is a very powerful energy which is fully utilized in radionic therapy. In fact, with some radionic instruments, thought appears to be able to override what has been set on the dials. It is, therefore, an energy to be controlled, or the value of the instruments will be lost.

These ideas may or may not be proved to be fact in the future but, for the present, we must be content with analogies with established scientific fact. For example, magnets show clearly how, under different conditions, energy patterns can be modulated. Magnets placed under iron filings will immediately make those iron filings move into repeatable patterns. Add another magnet and the pattern is altered at once.

The universal consciousness is beginning to be known and accepted through the work of people like Cleve Baxter, Marcel Vogel and the writings of Lyall Watson and Christopher Bird. They give examples of universal laws at work which suggest that the universe is an interconnected whole which operates in harmony. For instance, oysters, when taken inland, still change their feeding times to fit the changing times of the high tide and there is also evidence that animals know better than man when an earthquake is imminent. It is this interconnection which makes radionic therapy possible. The natural forces radionics employ are enhanced through the use of accurately designed instruments in conjunction with the radiesthetic faculty and the therapy has been shown to be effective from a distance of thousands of miles.

It is eight years now since the first edition of this book was published. My partner and co-author died in 1982 and much of my time has been concerned in furthering the cause of the Complementary Therapies through the founding of the Institute for Complementary Medicine.

The causes of ill health have changed dramatically over the past years. The principal reasons are no longer lack of hygiene and malnutrition, but far more subtle causes such as noise, stress, pollution of the environment, toxic additives to food, the side-effects of antibiotics, drug addiction, glue sniffing—even addiction to computers which has reduced some children to the state of nervous wrecks.

Dirt, infection and undernourishment are very much simpler to cope with than the modern day problems listed above which are largely being treated with drugs which give rise to new problems requiring drugs, and so on *ad infinitum*.

The limitation of orthodox medicine is fully exposed in an examination of the statistics. Hospital beds are full to overflowing, 25 per cent of these beds are occupied by patients suffering from the results of treatment.

The waiting list for operations is endless. The cost to the nation for drugs is astronomical and growing yearly; in 1984 the cost of drugs supplied to the N.H.S. was a staggering £1½ billion, and perhaps the main beneficiaries are the manufacturing drug houses rather than the patients.

The N.H.S. has accelerated the consumption of drugs because it is only human for people who have paid their contribution to wish to 'Get their money's worth' and to consider it their 'right' to have access to the latest wonder drugs even if they don't much like their side-effects.

The N.H.S. has done something else in its avowed policy of caring for everyone 'from the cradle to the grave'; people no longer feel responsible for their own health and the sturdy independent spirit which made this country one of the leading powers in the world has been sapped as a result.

Orthodox medicine is still looking at man much as a skilled mechanic regards a piece of machinery. Everything is known about the functions of the body down to the smallest cell. Specialists are adept at repairing and replacing defective organs in spare part surgery. Much is known about diseases but very little is known about man as a being. Invariably it is the disease that is treated and not the patient.

This mechanistic approach to medicine is outdated and must be replaced by a holistic concept more in keeping with the New Age that we have entered. Science and philosophy can co-operate in this new approach and basic causes of ill health should be sought out and countered rather than the suppression of the effects of illness.

Man is not a machine, he is a being of mind and spirit activated by a life force about which nothing is known, as elusive and indefinable as electricity and as easily accepted. One moment it is there and then—flash!—it has gone and all functions cease. The nature of man is a mystery which cannot be reduced to a 'nuts and bolts level'.

It is interesting that the theories put forward by radionic practitioners, for which they had only intuitive and empirical knowledge, are now being substantiated by scientific research which has reached the boundary which divides the physical from the non-physical and has started the probe into the non-physical aspect of matter.

One of the key beliefs upon which radionics is founded is that every individual has a unique energy pattern as particular to them as their fingerprint and it is this energy pattern which emanates from the witness and links the practitioner with the patient. Modern research has proved the truth of this and the unique patterns of D.N.A. in each individual has been demonstrated.

The Theory of Radionics

The theory of radionics is one of energy patterns, that is, the identification of the electrodynamic patterns emitted by matter of all kinds. The maintenance of health is believed to depend on the harmony of all the complex energy patterns that go to make up the human body. The balance of these energies and their relation to each other are most delicately poised and can be disorganized by intruding alien patterns of poisons, viruses or bacteria—even by strong emotions or negative thought. It seems clear that the level of consciousness does not stop with the mind but extends throughout all natural processes to cellular level. Each group of cells is conscious of its ordained function and, unless it is disorientated by some alien force, it pursues this function automatically. Should it be diverted from its proper behaviour disharmony and illness follow.

Modern medical practice seeks to introduce still more powerful agents to combat the invaders: radionic practice is aimed at reinforcing the natural energies or reversing the invading forces by sending them the mirror image of their own patterns. So it will be seen that radionic therapy seeks to use only natural forces to combat disease and this attempt to understand and co-operate with nature characterizes the development of this therapy.

The energy locked up in the atom has been forcibly demonstrated in our lifetime and as the atom is the building block of all matter, it can be said that a proper understanding and use of natural energies could be the most potent means of combating illness of all kinds. Nothing is more powerful than nature.

This theory of recognizable patterns has been substantiated by Dr Rupert Sheldrake in his hypothesis of formative causation. These patterns, termed Morphogenetic fields, are what Radionics is all about. It is these structures which make up the etheric counterpart body that we analyse and treat.

The etheric body is an exact replica in all respects to the physical form, but built of finer matter than the physical structure. It is as real as the physical body but more lasting. If a limb is amputated, or an organ excised, the etheric counterpart remains, which is why pain can sometimes be felt in a limb that is not there. We have taken photographs on the Radionic camera of a pair of lungs in a patient who had undergone surgery for the removal of one of them.

It is held that the etheric body survives death and passes on for a limited time before being discarded for an even finer substance.

Harold Saxton Burr has also postulated the existence of formative forces which he terms 'L' field, (the 'L' standing for 'Life'), which are outside space and time. He too believed that all individuals possess unique energy fields.

Whatever happens to the etheric body is reflected onto its physical counterpart—radionic treatment of the etheric can cause things to happen in the physical body which cannot be achieved by treating the physical body directly, it is a subtle and often a more effective approach with greater lasting results.

No claim is made that radionic treatment 'cures' a patient of his illness. It is always the patient's own life energy that brings about healing. The role of radionics is to discover the cause of the disease and to unblock the channels so that true energy can flow freely. Man is so designed that every cell knows its special function, and, given the free flow of energy, will perform it.

Acupuncture stimulates the flow of energy by the insertion of needles at appropriate points in the meridians. Radionics does the same thing by sending coded messages in numerical form to the source of the trouble. These messages are picked up and understood by the cells or groups of cells forming organs etc., so that blockages are cleared and the life energy flows freely again. The feedback from etheric to physical is instantaneous as this method of treatment appears to transcend both time and space. A patient in Australia will react as quickly as one close at hand. The constant flow of energy is essential to life, inertia is death.

Radionics is based on the understanding of man as a divine being, and reincarnation is part of this belief. It is held that the divine spark and the seed of perfection is inherent in every human being, but it takes many lifetimes to bring this to fruition.

If there is justice in the law of creation, reincarnation seems the only plausible answer. I look upon each lifetime on earth as a term at school and each death as a gateway to a holiday, although learning must surely continue even there. Some learn their lessons faster and easier than others. Some choose to learn the hard way and come back and back again to tackle the same tasks, but there is equal opportunity for all to progress towards ultimate perfection.

Some causes of illness are Karmic in origin, carried over from previous lives, and it is useless to try to suppress them as the lesson will remain unlearned and will have to be repeated. Help, on the other hand, can be given to the patient in tackling the problem and overcoming it.

Radionic therapy is a method of dealing radically with basic causative factors. It has the advantage of being able to explore all levels of the patient, be it man or beast—or indeed any living thing—in order to identify the root cause and location of the problem.

An added advantage is that it may be carried out at any distance from the patient without personal contact, thereby avoiding tension and psychological reactions which might distort the true picture of the condition.

This is particularly valuable in the case of animals who cannot tell us in words how they feel. Some human patients, on the other hand, may feel the need for personal contact and much counselling takes place over the telephone if distance prohibits meeting.

A very significant groundswell has become evident in the past few years and it is growing in momentum. More and more people are turning towards natural medicine, although it is not on the N.H.S. It was stated in the House of Lords in February 1985 that Complementary Medicine rated the second biggest growth industry in Britain, increasing by 15 per cent per annum, second only to computer technology. This makes it even more urgent that standards of training should be set for the many disciplines which are on offer so that the public can be protected from 'Cowboy Therapists' who may have taken a weekend course in a therapy which adepts have taken three or four years to learn.

The Institute for Complementary Medicine is attempting to establish a uniform standard of training common to all disciplines by setting up an independent education committee to which the training syllabus of any therapy can be submitted for approval.

Ideally this should be Government sponsored as it is to protect the public. The Institute has no axe to grind and is a charity devoted to improving health in all its aspects and initiating research into a new approach to illness and good health.

1. The Early Experiments

The radionic practitioner does not regard his patient as a creature of flesh and blood alone but as something infinitely more complex, comprising at least seven bodies of different and more ethereal structure. The one which concerns him most is the etheric body, being the counterpart body and precise duplicate of the material physical body. It is through the etheric body that the analysis is made and treatment is directed. This is an important fact as everything which is manifested in the physical body originates and is first detectable in the etheric body. This makes it possible to forecast and perhaps prevent illnesses when they are still in a pre-physical state.

A holistic approach to the patient—that is, regarding him as a being consisting of spirit, mind and body is essential. It is of little value to patch up the results of illness without seeking that cause; one might as well keep filling a leaking bucket without first mending the hole in it. Unless the cause, which may be spiritual, psychological or physical, is discovered and dealt with, the trouble will recur.

It is significant that in the very first experiments in making a radionic analysis the instrument used was the body of a healthy human being.

It was quite by chance that Dr Albert Abrams, a brilliant American neurologist, discovered that the human abdomen could be used as a diagnostic sounding board. He found that certain well-defined areas gave a dull instead of a hollow note when percussed if certain diseases were present. Further, the same signals could be detected when samples of diseased tissue in a container were connected to the healthy subject by a wire. (This only occurred, however, when the subject faced due west.) This is a phenomenon which has yet to be explained in scientific terms but Abrams knew that he had made a discovery of profound importance and from that moment all his energies and his considerable fortune were devoted to furthering research into this new and exciting field.

The task of being a human instrument proved wearing to the healthy young men who were required to stand facing west while the good doctor percussed their abdomens. After a two hour stint, they were so exhausted that their reactions became unreliable. Thus Abrams tried to find a substitute diagnostic instrument based on electronics rather than the nervous system. Not, possibly, as sensitive an instrument as the human body but more practical and not subject to fatigue. To this end, he sought help from electronic experts and even offered a reward of ten thousand dollars to anyone who could come up with the answer. But it was not to be in his lifetime and the human subject remained his only diagnostic instrument. Abrams' theory about why the percussion note changed when disease was present was that, since all matter is electrical in nature, specific radiations originating in diseased tissue affected nerve fibres, causing the muscle-contracting reflex in sharply defined areas. Having established that radiation from diseased tissue could travel down a wire and affect the nervous system of a healthy young man, he translated the different radiations of particular conditions into their specific resistances, accurately measured in ohms.

Radionic Instruments

Having satisfied himself that he was able to detect and diagnose disease, Abrams then turned his mind to producing a treatment instrument. He acquired the services of a talented inventor called Samuel Hoffman and together they produced an instrument they named the 'oscilloclast'. This instrument was powered by electricity and through it they were able to subject the patient to any one of ten different vibrational patterns by means of an electrode placed over the area of the spleen. The average treatment time was one hour and the patient had to return many times before he was cured. Nevertheless, considerable success was achieved and the medical profession was sharply divided into those few who were impressed by this revolutionary method, who took Abrams' postgraduate course and incorporated it in their practices, and those, in the majority, who decided the whole thing was a lot of poppycock.

Abrams would only teach qualified doctors and the few he taught soon found themselves busier than they had ever been before.

Abrams and his followers had considerable success with this treatment, crude though it may seem in relation to present day radionics. It is interesting to trace the progress from the beginning when the instrument was human but the treatment was electrical, up to the present day when both diagnosis and treatment employ a more subtle type of energy, which more closely resembles the natural forces emitted by all matter.

Those who followed Abrams, developed more sophisticiated instruments. The diagnostic abdomen was eventually replaced by a thin sheet of rubber stretched over a metal plate under which was an oblong cavity. The procedure was to stroke the rubber lightly with the fingers while altering the resistance by setting the dials to measurements of different disease conditions. When the resistance matched the radiation of the condition the rubber stuck to the fingers and diagnosis was established in the same way as the dull percussion note on the abdomen. This became known to practitioners as a 'stick pad'.

It was also discovered that they could treat their patients at a distance remote from the instrument and then that they could analyse the patient's condition from a spot of his blood on filter paper placed on the diagnostic instrument. This was clearly a great advantage to both practitioner and patient; especially when it was ascertained that distance made no difference to either the accuracy of the analysis or the efficiency of the treatment. If the practitioner was in London and the patient in Australia, there was an equal chance of success as if they had been in the same room.

Many different radionic instruments have been designed and put into use by Abrams' followers, notably Dr Guyon Richards, who carried out much painstaking research not only to improve the accuracy of the instruments but also into the scientific explanation of what they were doing. His measurements in ohms of elements as well as diseases were groping towards Dr Harold Burr's discovery many years later that all living forms are controlled by electrodynamic fields.

A Major Figure in Radionics
A major personality in the history of radionics was an American chiropractor called Ruth Drown who not only improved on the original instruments but also invented a radionic camera which

was able to take photographs of the insides of her patients at long range. When I visited her at her home in California in 1964, she showed me many photographs which she had taken, including some of the first Russian cosmonauts in orbit in their capsule and obviously weightless. The interesting thing about the photographs taken by this camera is that those taken by means of a blood spot at long range invariably showed a section through an organ or tissue, whereas those taken with the patient making contact with the camera showed a complete organ from an outside view.

Ruth Drown was a remarkable woman, deeply dedicated to radionics, very sincere and extremely intuitive. Unprejudiced by scientific training she approached the subject with an open and enquiring mind and came, perhaps closer than any other radionic inventor, to an understanding of the true nature of radionics. She returned to Abrams' original concept that the human being was the finest instrument and extended this to include treatment as well as diagnosis. Her concept was that it was the life force of the patient that carried out the healing and the job of the practitioner was to channel and direct this force to the parts of the body that needed it. Her treatment started with a daily evaluation of the functioning of the endocrine glands which she considered of prime importance. She devised a complex analysis sheet which was completed for every patient. On this she evaluated the function of all systems, made a blood count and urine analysis, measured the blood pressure and built up a complete picture of the physical state of the individual before treatment. Her instruments are no longer much used but her 'rates' or dial settings are still used on more modern instruments.

Ruth Drown died a martyr to the cause of radionics in 1966. Harrassed by both the medical profession and the Food & Drugs Administration of the State of California, she was accused of fraud and, in spite of conclusive evidence given by the patients she had healed, the verdict went against her on the ground that her instruments were 'not scientifically able' to achieve the results that she and her patients claimed for them.

Her instruments were confiscated and destroyed and her appeal against the verdict and her counterclaims for compensation for defamation of character and loss of livelihood dragged on for many years, without reaching any conclusion. She was finally imprisoned for a short time and her life was in ruins. She suffered two strokes and lived for only a short time after the second one. It is open to speculation how much the vested interests of the drug houses played in this action but it is certain that the name of Ruth Drown will live on in the memory of anyone interested in radionics, both for her heroic stand against undeserved adversity and for the understanding which she brought to this therapy.

The Delawarr Camera

It was one of her instruments which started the next chapter of radionics. In Oxford, George de la Warr, a civil engineer, was asked to make a copy of a Drown diagnostic instrument as imports from the United States in war time were not possible. George de la Warr, known to his friends as Bill, was an imaginative man with an enquiring mind. The concept of this instrument fired his curiosity and he became so intrigued that he gave up his career in engineering and devoted his considerable skill and energies to furthering the cause of radionics in the United Kingdom. He designed and produced many new instruments, all of them immaculately made, and carried out endless experiments incorporating the use of colour, light and sound. Ideas would tumble over each other in his fertile mind and it is possible that some of his best ideas were lost in the rush of those that followed after.

Bill always aimed to use the natural forces that surrounded him and these he sought to harness by ingenious mechanical contrivances. I can remember one happy afternoon spent in his garden capturing the sound pattern of a common daisy on a tape recorder. Bill de la Warr was greatly helped by his wife, Marjorie, who was a very sensitive and intuitive woman, also entirely engrossed in radionics and a skilled practitioner.

Bill also invented a camera which was able to take photographs at extreme distances. It was quite different from the Drown camera and the pictures it obtained from a blood spot of the patient were of the entire organs, unless the dials were turned to conditions in the blood or tissues in which case an overall pattern showed on the plate. I own one of the very few Delawarr cameras that were made. They had to be custom built for those who were to use them and varied in measurement according to the forcefield of the operators. My instrument stands just under five feet high and two feet square. The procedure is to load a plate into the slide, set the diagnosed condition and the part of the body that it was affecting on the dials, place the slide in the upper part of the camera, exposing the plate to the inside of the camera then, standing on two sides of the apparatus and concentrating on the patient, a switch is depressed setting off three vibrators in the bottom half of the camera. After a count of ten, the plate is taken out and developed. All this takes place in total darkness and it is important that no light whatever reaches the plate either in the camera or the dark room until fixing has been completed. If our diagnosis was correct, we would get a clearly recognizable picture of the organ affected and the severity of the condition was assessed by the blackness of the image. If our diagnosis was incorrect, only a faint and shadowy picture resulted.

We were living in London at that time and every month we would have a photographic day, checking our findings of the past weeks.

A Mysterious Discovery

Leonard Corté, who worked at the Delawarr Laboratory, would come up from Oxford and spend the day in our bathroom loading and developing plates, while we set the camera and lined up each side to take the picture. This was a very useful check on the accuracy of our findings and all went well until one day when Leonard was prevented from coming and we attempted to carry out all procedures on our own. Blank plate after blank plate were the only results of our efforts—not even a clouded plate but clear glass, so we rang Bill and told him that the camera had gone wrong. Leonard duly came up and we had another session of excellent pictures and this was the first hint that there was an unknown factor in this piece of equipment which was dependent on the presence of Leonard. As long as he touched the plates either before or after they had been exposed in the camera, we got a picture. If he had not touched them we got a blank plate.

We tried many experiments, but the mystery is still unresolved. We got him to handle a number of plates before he returned to Oxford and found that the sensitivity was ephemeral and only lasted about two hours. We had him leave his finger tips on plates in the darkroom for varying lengths of time and if he left them there too long, the whole plate was blackened. There appeared to be some force which flowed involuntarily from him and which sensitized the emulsion. We tried many different people but without any comparable results.

A very few other individuals *have* succeeded in getting a picture, notably Houghton Bentley but none could ever guarantee good results like Leonard.

Bill was working on still other ideas when he died, suddenly, of a heart attack in 1969; his widow, Marjorie, died in 1985.

In the celebrated 'Black Box Case' in 1960, Bill was charged with fraud by a lady named Miss Phillips, who claimed that she had been reduced to a state of neurosis in trying to operate one of his diagnostic instruments.

It was as patently false as the case brought against Ruth Drown in the United States since it had never been claimed that the diagnostic was a machine but only that it was an instrument which a skilled operator could use to good purpose. It would have been equally silly to sue a violin maker for selling a violin upon which the purchaser was unable to play a tune. Miss Phillips never completed her training in radionics and was obviously lacking the requisite skills and sensitivity ever to make an operator.

It was interesting that the Judge, Mr Justice Davies, while dismissing all allegations of fraud and upholding Bill as a man of integrity, sincerity and honesty, was, at the same time, unable to accept the viability of the radionic camera. We were both in the witness box for a considerable time and I produced some photographic plates which we had taken of my patients' conditions. The prosecuting counsel, Mr David Karmel, Q.C., called an expert witness to prove that it was possible to produce a similar effect by painting the images on the wet emulsion in the dark room. I had visions of the good lady toiling away all through the luncheon break with her wet brush in a dark room, painting images of hearts, lungs and intestines and then developing the results which seemed so very difficult and tedious compared to Leonard's method of dropping the plate in the developing dish and sloshing it about until the images appeared. Leonard is a very clever man but how he could have known what image to paint, as we never told him what we were taking, is difficult to say. I was reproved by Mr Karmel for smiling in the witness box but it struck me as irresistibly · funny. One day, the 'Leonard factor' in the camera will no doubt be explained in scientific terms and maybe resolved.

Bill de la Warr won his case but was landed with crippling costs, as Miss Phillips had brought the case on legal aid, and could not pay them. The law has since been changed to deal with this situation.

Figure 1. The late Malcolm Rae, to whom this book is dedicated.

Malcolm Rae

The next major figure in the radionic scene was Malcolm Rae, who brought a new concept to both instruments and treatment. His approach was rational and his research meticulous. His capacity for work seemed to be endless. When he first started working in radionics in 1961, he was managing a large car hire firm in London and his radionic research was carried out late at night and in the small hours of the morning. For some years, he cut his sleep down to three or four hours in the twenty-four, in order to delve deeply into the cure of illness by radionics. Malcolm believed that the correct answer to any question that may be asked is inherent in the 'collective unconscious' and all that is required to obtain these answers is that the questions should be clear and precise and the mind of the questioner unclouded by any bias. An expert operator of the pendulum, Malcolm wrote every question down before asking it and the stacks of notebooks recording both questions and answers are witness to the meticulous method of his work. Roget's Thesaurus was his constant companion and if a clear answer was not forthcoming to a question, he would rephrase it, changing a word here and there until the meaning was crystal clear and the answer unequivocal.

He had the rare quality of a completely lucid and objective mind and was never satisfied with anything less than the best. Every problem was investigated in depth and the resulting information has brought a new understanding to the reality of this work.

In a paper which he read to the British Society of Dowsers, he described his methods and some of his findings. In paying tribute to the advance of science he said that it had now reached the limit of the capacity to measure ultra high frequency energy patterns.

In a survey of scientific opinion, when 1,500 scientists were questioned, seventy per cent of them accepted the reality of extrasensory perception and this gives authoritative support for the use of the human instrument as a detection device. The human instrument, as was suspected by Dr Abrams and Ruth Drown, is superior to any made by man, if properly used. The scope of the radiesthetic sense is very extensive and can be used to detect and measure thought patterns. Yet the human instrument is extremely delicately balanced and subject to self-limitation. A lack of confidence will inhibit proper function. We all know that the expectation of one's own failure is often self-fulfilling.

There may be confusion between intuition and imagination. Each have their part to play, imagination and intellect combine to form the questions, intuition provides the answers which are then evaluated by intellect.

From this it will be appreciated that very strict control must be maintained in order to reach the truth, which is our objective at all times. Malcolm devised one aid which has proved useful in the form of a sheet of rubber permeated with small magnetic particles which, when placed under a chart, lessens intellectual activity and cuts out preconceived ideas. The other instruments he invented have proved to be an invaluable asset to the development of radionics.

Some knowledge of the subject under investigation is essential in order that relevant questions can be asked and this is why all students of radionics are required to have a working knowledge of anatomy and physiology.

Malcolm made a deep study of the way in which radionics works and he felt that thought can be crystallized either numerically or geometrically and that controlled breathing can act as a carrier of thought. There is a well known saying that 'energy follows thought' but it seems more likely that thought *is* energy. Here may lie the explanation of such phenomena as telepathy.

Nearly all radionic instruments have a magnet in them and this acts as an accumulator, transducer and radiator and both holds and sends out the energy pattern set on the dials.

If man could only develop his full potential, instruments would become obsolete but we are a very long way off achieving this yet and in the meantime we must make use of the props that people like Malcolm can devise for us to use as an aid to healing.

This is the way that Malcolm's instruments were designed and built. The calibration of the dials was refined to cover forty-four possible settings on each dial, instead of the previous eleven, so that a more exact geometrical pattern could be produced. The efficiency of this instrument was such that treatment time on any one rate was reduced from one hour to 2.2 minutes.

Much of his research was carried out with a doctor and his instruments are now widely used in medical practice throughout the world.

The Potency Simulator

One of Malcolm's most remarkable inventions was his 'magnetogeometric potency simulator' (see Figure 7) which employs geometrical drawings printed on cards which slip into a slot in the instrument which is fitted with a circular magnet. These drawings consist of seven concentric circles from which a variable number of division lines, in critical positions, point to its centre. There are currently some ten thousand of these cards, representing a vast range of homoeopathic remedies, human organs, functions and diseases.

The 'potency simulator' can be used in two ways; either to subject the patient directly to the energy pattern by placing a witness of the patient in the well of the instrument, or to impregnate the required energy pattern into distilled water or inert sac lac tablets placed in the well and taken orally by the patient. In both cases the exact potency of the remedy to be given is first established by means of the pendulum and set on the dial of the simulator.

Since beginning work on the first edition of this book, Malcolm, tragically, died and radionics suffered a great loss. It is impossible to overestimate the value of his work during the nineteen years which he devoted to it. His untiring energy and imaginative purpose raised radionics to a new dimension and he will live on in his great contributions to this work. We dedicated this book to his memory, with most grateful thanks.

Instrumentation is now becoming simpler rather than more complicated. In the past, inventors have designed some instruments which resemble a console with up to one hundred dials. The latest and most sophisticated instruments are small and unassuming with very few dials but very great accuracy and the impact of treatment on the patient is sharper and quicker. The analysis too is more immediate and takes much less time than the old methods. When we started in practice in the early 1950's, the analysis of a single patient took many hours, sometimes more than a day. Now the measurement of the condition of a patient and the discrepancy of the functioning of all systems against optimum perfection, can be completed in less than one hour at the end of which time we have what is virtually a 'blueprint' of the patient on all levels.

It must be emphasized that the functioning of all instruments is entirely dependent on the sensitivity and skill of the operator. They do not work on their own. They act almost as extensions of the operator because they hold and respond to his thoughts.

If we had learned to use the full potential of our minds, instruments would not be necessary but, alas, we have as yet, only learned how to use one tenth of our brains and the strain of holding a thought in absolute clarity and providing the energy to project it to the patient, would strictly limit our usefulness. With the aid of instruments we can help many more people than would be possible without them.

2. Training

Training in radionics is by no means easy, as, although specially designed instruments are used in analysis and treatment, they are valueless unless they are used with skilled understanding and relaxed attention which is a discipline which takes a great deal of patient practice to perfect.

It is all too easy to allow personal opinions and desires to creep in and cloud the issue, thereby making the findings valueless because they are not true.

The first lesson that the student has to learn is that the search for truth is paramount in making an analysis and that it does not matter how unpleasant the truth may be, because the only way to help the patient is to face the facts and find the root cause of the problem for only when this is determined can it be tackled and eliminated.

The Pendulum

Perhaps the most vital piece of equipment of the practitioner's aids is the pendulum and this is the first instrument he must learn to use. There is a special art in using a pendulum which not everyone possesses. It requires a sensitivity similar to that of using a divining rod to find water or minerals. It is a discipline which develops with much practice and it is not always easy as it requires a very clear mind when posing the question and a lack of all tension and the elimination of any emotion or preconceived ideas which might influence the answer. It is all too easy at first, when seeking 'causes', to dread finding such things as malignancy and to allow the subconscious to influence the findings. Again, it is simple to lose concentration and allow the mind to wander for a vital moment

Figure 2. The Pendulum.

in which time you may get the answer to some quite irrelevant thought which has popped up in the subconscious. The object throughout is to get the truth whatever it may be.

The technique is to set the pendulum swinging freely and, having established the signal for 'yes' and 'no', relax and note its response. The swing of the pendulum is governed by a neuro-muscular reaction which feels like a mild electric shock running down the arm. We are often asked where the pendulum gets the answer from and the best answer is from the 'collective unconscious mind'— that great pool of all knowledge which is accessible to all who ask in truth.

This fact has been brought into the scientific field by Dr Rupert Sheldrake and Lyall Watson, who have supplied evidence of the existence of a reservoir of knowledge comprising all the experience of man through the ages and into which is fed, at intervals, new knowledge not devised by man but emanating from some superior source as man is considered fit to use it. This would seem to explain how it is that similar new discoveries appear from quite disconnected researchers at the same time.

Animals too, have their own 'collective unconscious' reservoirs fed by the experiences and memories of their own kind. It is probable that they have much easier access to their reservoirs than we do to ours as they have not been 'educated away' from the natural world as we have. They know instinctively how to build nests and burrows, where to go in the different seasons, and how to return to the place where they were born.

That new information is available and is utilized by creatures of the same species is illustrated by Lyall Watson's story of the tribe of monkeys which started a new social habit of washing food before eating it; no sooner had this custom been established than other troops of monkeys showed the same new behaviour pattern, although they were remote from the originators of the discovery.

We all contribute to knowledge after our own kind and we all can draw from it at will.

The standard pendulum with which all students are trained is of conical shape in clear resin, containing a seven coil wire spiral.

The way this came about is, perhaps, worth relating. I had an extremely vivid dream one night in which I saw myself making just such a pendulum. This was something which I had not ever thought about but the dream was so vivid that I felt moved to see whether I could bring it to reality, and by trial and error, I finally achieved it and asked Malcolm Rae to try it out. Not only did Malcolm approve it but he suggested that if the coil was wound on the Golden Mean Ratio, it would be even more sensitive. This has now been done and the pendulum is a literal example of something which has been 'dreamed up'.

Having mastered the use of the pendulum, students are assigned to a tutor who is qualified to teach both the philosophy of Radionics and the method of analysis, together with the operation of the many different instruments which are available for analysis and treatment. No student can commence training before passing an examination in human biology, as analysis depends on a question and answer technique, and it is not possible to ask the right questions without a knowledge of human anatomy and physiology.

Looking back on the history of Radionics an interesting pattern emerges. We see that it started on quite orthodox lines of physical medicine, albeit by unorthodox means. Dr Abrams was working with disease tissues and bacteria. He was a highly qualified doctor, a professor of Pathology and Director of Clinical Medicine. He was no 'fly by night' dreamer, but a greatly gifted medical man dissatisfied with the existing methods of diagnosis. His work proceeded on strictly physical and scientific lines, he was dealing in electronics and measured disease reaction in ohms. He would teach only qualified doctors in the use of his methods.

It was Dr Ruth Drown, an American chiropractor who shifted the emphasis from the physical to the non-physical aspect of illness and health. This stemmed from her insistence that the endocrine system played the primary role in health and that stimulation of the centres governing the glands brought about healing by the patients own life energy.

It was she who discovered that effective healing could be given from distances remote from the patient although her analysis was always conducted with the physical presence of the patient whose feet were placed on metal plates attached to the diagnostic instrument.

Funnily enough, George Delawarr who led the development of Radionics in the U.K. stuck to the physical and scientific approach, and did not introduce subtle anatomy into his teaching apart from holding that Radionic treatment acted on the etheric body rather than on the physical.

During the last decade radionics has moved steadily forward into a more spiritual approach; ever more emphasis is placed on the importance of the energy centres which are non-physical vortexes of force termed 'chakras' which lie along the back of the spine of the etheric body and govern the functions of the endocrine glands upon which the health of the individual depends.

Everything that happens in the etheric body is reflected in the physical body, whether it be good or bad. The energy pattern of a disease is quickly translated to the physical, so is the pattern of healing. Neither body can function independently as they are indivisible until death when the etheric counterpart withdraws and continues its existence elsewhere.

Progress in the practice of radionics has been somewhat impaired by having been dominated by part-time lay practitioners. This is not to say that these individuals have not done much good work and been of lasting benefit to a great many patients, but it has tended to restrict practitioners to amateur status and led to them being disregarded by the trained and qualified professionals in the more widely accepted therapies.

There is a need for greater professionalism in radionics than has been seen so far. If it is to take its rightful place in the ranks of the healing arts it must set its sights much higher and pursue a more rigorous training programme than it has done in the past. This is already being put into effect.

I believe it has an enormous potential in maintaining health which must not be dissipated by a casual approach. An increasing number of paramedics are now using radionics in their practices and the need for fully trained professional radionic practitioners is paramount.

A training period of at least three years is essential to qualify students starting from scratch and any attempt to cut corners and carry out crash courses can only lead to a denigration of the whole profession. I have been practising for thirty years, and I am still learning.

It takes deep study and dedication to master the many facets of radionics but it is fascinating and rewarding work.

3. Radionic Analysis

The technique of making a radionic analysis, has changed radically since the days of Abrams and Drown and, indeed, it is still changing as better methods are found. This is natural and right. Radionics is a new science and still has much to learn. If it were to remain static it would surely die of inertia and never reach its full potential for healing. As it is, the growth of radionics has been steady over the years and the persecution of its pioneers has in no way affected the progress it has made.

In detailing the present technique of making an analysis I am very conscious that it may be quite outdated by the time the reader picks up the book but I can only give the method used at the time of writing.

The Witness
The witness commonly used is a lock of the patient's hair. The bloodspot had been discarded as it had been found that if the patient had a blood transfusion, the original bloodspot no longer related to him.

We found this out the hard way. A patient of mine was in hospital having had a prostate operation and so successful had I been in saving him from post-operative shock and so diligent in keeping him cheerful and confident, that his surgeon was misled in thinking that he was fit to get up and go for a walk long before he should have done. The scar broke down and the poor man had a severe haemorrhage and was whisked smartly back to bed and given a massive transfusion. I was informed of this by the patient's wife and hastily put him on appropriate emergency treatment. Next morning I settled down at my desk to investigate how he was

progressing and to my utter horror my pendulum instead of
swinging briskly to give the signals of 'yes' or 'no' to my questions,
it hung stationary over the blood spot and stubbornly refused to
swing in any direction. This, to my mind, meant only one thing:
my patient was dead.

Quick to jump to the wrong conclusions, I inevitably took the
blame for this unfortunate occurrence, telling myself that it was
all my fault for having healed the patient too quickly and thereby
bringing about his premature death. I felt unable to ring up his
sorrowing widow and as he was a well known person whose death
would not escape the public eye, I opened my morning paper in
fear and trepidation.

After several days had passed with no news of his death, it was
suggested that I might substitute the patient's signature. This I did
and the response was lively and immediate. In this way we
discovered the unreliability of blood spots and substituted a lock
of hair as a witness as this remains constant and continues to provide
a valid link throughout a lifetime. The patient made an excellent
recovery.

There is another advantage in using hair instead of blood for
people like ourselves who are squeamish about sticking needles
into our patient's fingers. Whenever possible, we used to give the
patient a sterilized needle and a bit of blotting paper and invite
them to perform the act himself. This often did not work as the
patients were as squeamish as we were so we bought a special
instrument, rather like a cigar cutter with a sharp point activated
by a spring. This was almost too effective and called for sticking
plaster to stop the bleeding so you can imagine our relief when
all that was required was a pair of scissors and one painless snip
of a lock of hair.

Even this has its hazards as I discovered to my cost. One dear
old lady requiring treatment for a rheumatic condition, bridled
when I asked if I might cut a snip of her hair and seemed reluctant.
I assured her that I only required a small piece and it would not
show and the witness was duly procured. The trouble was that
I never knew whose witness it was as the lady was wearing a wig
and was too proud to admit it!

The method of preparing a witness is to stick a few hairs between
two circular tacky labels and to write the name of the patient on
the outside. The shape of the label seems to be important as it

ensures that the witness remains in resonance with the patient constantly wherever he may be and whatever he may be doing. A rectangular label may go in and out of phase and has been found less reliable. As soon as the witness is placed on the instrument a living link is established with the patient.

Subtle Anatomy

The first step in making an analysis is to find out whether the etheric, astral or mental bodies are suffering from congestion, over-stimulation or aberration. The etheric is concerned with the physical body, the astral is concerned with emotions and the mental is concerned with the spiritual dimension of man. The Nadis, which is the etheric counterpart of the central nervous system, must also be checked for these conditions. Finally, in this part of the analysis, a check is made to see whether there is any lack of co-ordination between the physical and etheric bodies and the astral and mental bodies as any disharmony here may be an important cause in ill health.

It is due to the work of David Tansley that the subtle anatomy aspect of radionics has become so important. It has long been recognized that we are not dealing directly with gross physical structures but rather with their etheric counterparts but it was not until the publication of David Tansley's first book on subtle anatomy (see *Further Reading*) that it was incorporated as an integral part of each analysis.

His study of man's subtle anatomy follows the teachings of the ancient philosophers who placed the highest importance on the non-physical aspect of man's nature and described in detail the seven planes which comprise all human beings. The etheric body, which we as practitioners are most concerned with, is described as consisting of fine energy threads or lines of force and light. It is, in fact, an energy field permeating and interpenetrating the whole of the physical body. The seven main chakras or force centres are the focal points through which the physical body is energized. Each of the main chakras bears a special relationship with an endocrine gland which in turn controls a particular area of the body and it is essential to health that all chakras should be kept free of blockages so that energy may flow and proper balance may be maintained.

As well as the seven principal chakras there are twenty-one minor chakras and forty-nine focal points of energy. It is clear therefore,

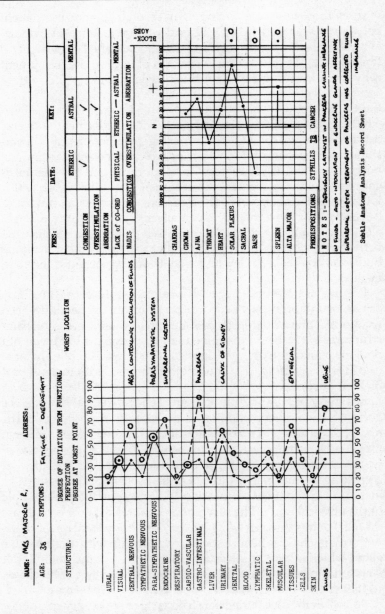

Figure 3. Subtle Anatomy Record Sheet.

that an understanding of the subtle anatomy is vital in making an analysis of every patient as any imbalance will inevitably lead to pathological illness. These chakras are delicately balanced and can be affected by violent accidents, shock of all kinds and strong emotions or negative thought. When blockages occur and the life energy ceases to flow through to the corresponding endocrine glands there is an inevitable physical reaction. Thus the second step in analysis is to measure the patient's energy centres and to record the extent of any deviation from normal on the analysis chart.

Man is dependent on the flow of energy through his chakras as much as all life on this planet depends on the energy of the sun but because chakras cannot be seen, except perhaps by a clairvoyant, and cannot be dissected or observed under a microscope, they have been discounted by medical science. Orthodox medicine's mechanistic view of man is short-sighted and distorted. It is only when all aspects—physical, emotional and spiritual are considered together that a true understanding of the individual as a whole can emerge.

It is for this reason that an integral part of any analysis is to measure the deviation of all the energy centres of chakras from the norm and when the analysis of the physical structures is completed the two halves can be related to each other as a whole and a logical picture is revealed.

In this analysis we pick up traces of inherited diseases which show up as predispositions towards such things as cancer, syphilis and tuberculosis. This analysis demonstrates the reality of the dictum that 'the sins of the fathers are visited on the children'. They are the taints carried in the genes from father to son and although they may never be manifested in the physical, they indicate a weakness and a tendency towards a particular illness.

Diagnosing Causes

Next we turn to the systems of the body measuring the function of each one against optimal perfection. Here the aim is to measure the deviation of the function from perfect and, in particular, the extent of the deviation of the worst point in each system—for example, the skeletal system as a whole may show a 30° deviation from functional perfection but the worst point in that system may be 80°. This means that within the skeletal system, there is one bone, joint or vertebra which is 80° away from perfection. There

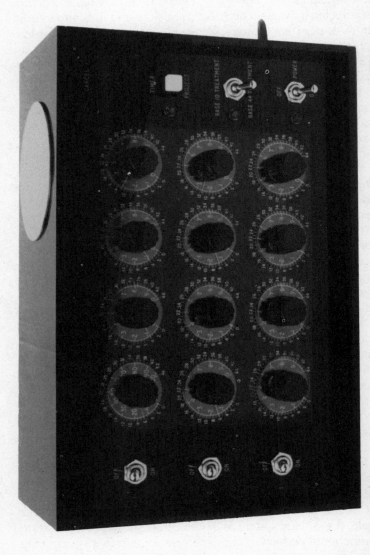

Figure 4. The Rae Base 44 treatment instrument, each bank operates independently, the witness is placed on the circular plate on top, treatment time is 2.2 minutes.

may be several parts which show imperfection between the 30° and 80° and sometimes there is no 'worst point' but the whole system may be faulty. When all the measurements of the system have been made, the exact locations of any 'worst point' which deviates 50° or more are identified.

All this is plotted on graph paper and on completion is easily read and can be compared to the corresponding pattern of the subtle anatomy variations. The whole makes a complete picture of the state of the patient on all levels.

It is now important to find the causes which underlie the pattern which has emerged from the energy centres, systems and the worst locations. In order to measure all these things, the dials of the Base-44 instrument mentioned in Chapter 1 are set for whatever is being measured but when finding the worst locations, the question and answer technique is used. The practitioner asks a mental question, for example, 'which is the worst location in the skeletal structure', and reads down a list of locations within the structure until the pendulum indicates an affirmative.

He does the same, when finding causes. The patient's witness is placed on the circular disc on the instrument but no dial settings are used.

Analysis and Treatment

Having found the causes, a complete blueprint of the patient is at hand and the question then arises as to what treatment should be given.

Again, the witness is placed on the round disc of the instrument with no dial settings and the practitioner asks whether the first treatment should be one from the etheric, astral, mental section or an energy centre. If no affirmative is obtained to any of these, he turns to the treatment sheet in the rate book and reads down the list of possible radionic treatments. This must be done carefully as it sometimes happens that the eye is quicker than the brain and a 'yes' signal is obtained when the practitioner is still pondering the previous line. When inaccurate results are obtained, the practitioner must brush up his awareness and test the written words again.

Usually, more than one radionic treatment is required on the instrument and having found all that are required on that day, it is necessary to ask if any other treatment should be given. The patient may require medical treatment, osteopathy, homoeopathy or may need treatment on a different type of radionic instrument.

It is vital that the practitioner ensures that all necessary questions have been asked both in making the analysis and in finding the right treatment. Only then can the patient be filed away for that day.

The Rae Analyser

It sounds a very long process and indeed it can be but with practice it can be speeded up and, through the use of the Rae Analyser, which will now be described, the time needed has been greatly reduced.

The Rae Analyser uses geometric cards instead of 'rates' set on dials. There are many thousands of these cards representing structures, named diseases and remedies. These cards emit an energy

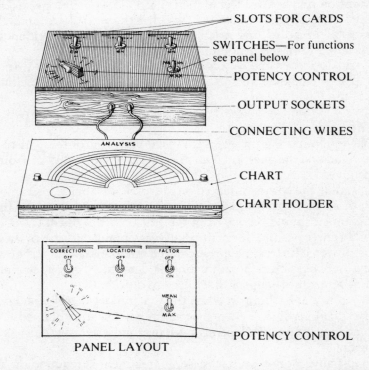

Figure 5. The Rae Analyser. It must be emphasized that the operation of this instrument is dependent upon the radiesthetic sensitivity of the user.

pattern in the same way as the dial settings but the advantage of their use is that they are all drawn with extreme accuracy and there is no danger of careless setting on the instrument as their value is constant. It also takes much less time to slip a card into a slot than to set a series of dials.

A detailed description of making an analysis on this instrument is given in David Tansley's book *Dimensions of Radionics* (see *Further Reading*), so I will only dwell on the difference in making an analysis on these two instruments.

The Rae Analyser consists of two parts, connected with wires. The main part is equipped with three slots into which the cards representing causes, locations and remedies are placed, each slot having its own controlling switch. There is also a potency control. The other part of the analyser comprises a chart holder which takes the interchangeable charts for analysis and treatment.

In making the analysis, the cards for the centres and structures are inserted in turn and their variations from perfect functions are measured and noted. We end up with the same graph as we did with the other method but in a much shorter time. Treatment is found by noting the swing of a pendulum towards different sections of the treatment chart which contain all possible treatments from surgery to homoeopathic remedies. It may be that the patient would benefit from acupuncture, osteopathy, diet or vitamins or, perhaps, allopathic medicine.

Treatment

Patients are all different and react differently to alternative therapies. There is no set rule for treatment of any condition. Every patient is unique. If the indication is for a homoeopathic remedy to be given, first the initial letter of the remedy is found on the chart and then a pointer is run down a list of all remedies starting with that letter until the pendulum indicates the one required.

The card for this remedy is then slipped into the 'correction' slot and if it balances out the card in the 'factor' slot, that is the correct remedy. The potency dial is turned to 10mm and moved slowly backwards until the pendulum signals the correct potency.

The Rae Simulator is then set to this potency, the card is inserted in the 'project' slot. The patient's witness is placed in the well and the interrupter is switched on to project the remedy to the patient.

The energy pattern of the remedy will flow immediately from

Figure 6. The Rae Potency Simulator. Gives treatment via cards potentizing remedies or direct to patient using the interrupter and a patient's sample.

the card to the etheric body of the patient, wherever he may be. Sometimes it is more beneficial to the patient to be given the remedy to take orally in which case sac lac tablets are energized with the pattern of the remedy and are sent to him. There may be a psychological aspect in this, that some patients can more readily accept treatment if it is seen to be given in a physical sense and therefore receive greater benefit from it, if it is backed by their own positive thought. Nothing is more certain than the fact that it is impossible to heal a patient of any condition if he does not wish to be healed. This may be on a subconscious level but it is as effective a barrier as conscious negative thought.

Having given the initial treatment, the process is repeated to determine what else is required; if the patient should be placed on any other instrument, put on a diet or sent to an osteopath etc.

Every case is fully documented and every treatment is recorded in the patient's file along with the case history which he has filled in before starting treatment.

The Role of Faith

It is interesting that the patient's belief or lack of belief in radionics, in no way affects the success of the treatment. All that is necessary is that he desires full health and wishes to be rid of his disabilities. On many occasions we have had patients who have confessed that they cannot believe that radionics can help where Harley Street has failed but, as they are desperate, they are prepared to try anything—even us. These individuals respond to treatment equally well as those who come with all faith, confident that they will be helped. Indeed, in some ways we prefer them as they present a challenge and are less likely to be impatient like those expecting an immediate 'cure'. We have had cases of individuals who have been crippled for years and who give up treatment in disgust because they are not better in a month.

As a rule, the cases which have taken years to develop are slow to clear and the acute conditions which have progressed rapidly, or are caught at an early stage, can be eliminated equally quickly. The only part that faith plays in this therapy is the faith of the practitioner in what he is doing. The longer he has been in practice, and the more evidence he has had of its effect, the greater his faith in his work. Students starting on their careers as radionic therapists are, without exception, astonished by their first successes and indeed, this wonderment does not cease even after years in practice.

We are often told categorically that what we are doing is really faith healing and that our success is only due to our patient's belief in our work. This is not born out either by the patients who come to us in desperation and unbelieving or by the animals who are totally unaware of our intervention in their lives and who respond to treatment better than humans with a success rate of ninety per cent against the eighty per cent success rate of their masters.

Colour Therapy

We have very many different instruments in our repertoire and they all have some particular facet of healing which is helpful in some cases. We use colour quite extensively and each different shade has its own particular quality and effect. Blue, for instance, is soothing and relieves pain. Red and orange are stimulating and green is cleansing and healing. We have special instruments which have provision for the use of colour filters in addition to dials. Colour is an important factor in daily life. We all know the effect that different colours have on us whether it be in our own homes or in our choice of clothes. Try working in an office painted bilious green or muddy brown and your spirits will sink to zero.

Schools, hospitals and some factories have discovered the dynamic effect that colour has on health, harmony and production and one famous drug firm, whose factory we visited, had solved their production problems by merely changing the colour scheme of the décor and the women's overalls to a matching pink.

The Peggotty Board
Another instrument which we use to good effect is one of the

Figure 7. Peggotty Board.

Figure 8. Simulator Type Remedy/Location.

simplest both in concept and design. Nicknamed 'Peggotty', because it resembles a peg board, it has no magnets or electricity but a geometric pattern is set up by the accurate placement of black pegs on a white perspex ground. If the treatment is correct for the patient, it will even reduce displacement in a joint. The late Mr Butcher designed and made this remarkable instrument which bears no relation to any other piece of radionic equipment and appears to be a 'one-off' in direct inspiration. Few radionic practitioners would care to be without this instrument and I have some forty of them in continual use in my practice.

Simulator Type Remedy/Location
The last Rae designed instrument, and it is a very exciting one, has speeded up the process of treatment in a variety of cases.

In a sense it is like using a Peggotty or 9 Dial but with quicker results and it seems to be able to give a great variety of treatments.

To give a few examples, there are special cards such as Elimination, Detoxify, Optimalize which are not much use on their own but to be able to use Elimination for infection or a cyst, or an irritation or a specific toxin such as Herpes (or, indeed almost any condition), is of inestimable value. Detoxify seems also to be an outstandingly useful card and it has been used to get rid of a very bad eye irritation where the lid swelled up from an insect bite. After one treatment of 4 minutes, the swelling subsided and so did the irritation. This card has also been used effectively on patients with coughs by detoxifying lungs and bronchi and sinuses have cleared up by detoxifying sinuses. There is no end to the examples that can be given on the use of these two cards. What is particularly interesting is that where it has looked obvious that the Elimination card should be used and in fact the Detoxify one has been indicated, the patient has reacted very quickly and has therefore shown once again that the practitioner must not use his own knowledge or mind but must ask through the pendulum what treatment is indicated.

The Optimalize card is used almost entirely in conjunction with organs, for example, optimalizing the liver or lungs. Occasionally, however, the treatment has been to optimalize sight or Life Energy.

Interrupter

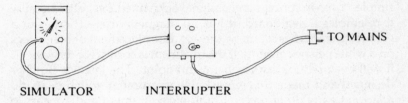

SIMULATOR   INTERRUPTER

Figure 9. Shows how the interrupter connects the simulator and the mains.

This instrument is linked with the mains electricity and the Rae Potency Simulator or Simulator Type Remedy/Location. It is only used when giving treatment to a patient with the patients sample, i.e. hair in a disc, in the well and therefore at a distance. It is not used when making a potentized remedy of sac lac or distilled water.

Its object is to produce a rapid pulsation which enhances the treatment. Each time a treatment is given on either instrument the required potency is set and the interrupter is switched on for the length of time of the treatment.

Sound Therapy
Then there are the nine dial instruments that use sound to give extra 'punch' to the treatment rates set on the dials. These incorporate a vibrator inside the case which, when switched on

Figure 10. Delawarr 12 Dial Treatment Instrument.

to the mains, gives a constant buzz. Having discovered by question and answer that an interrupted buzz was more effective than one that was constant, we fitted an army surplus bomb timing device into the circuit with very satisfactory results.

We did indeed invent some quite different instruments of our own. One very large one was equipped with ten tuning forks which were struck rhythmically by piano hammers powered by a small electric motor. Each note represented a planet, as related in a fascinating book called, *The Theory of Celestial Harmony* by Rodney Collins. It is his contention that every planet exerts an influence over particular organs or systems of the human body. The moon, for instance, controls the genital system and the circulation of fluids and the planet Mercury influences the respiratory system. In order to use this instrument, we had first to cast the patient's horoscope to find out which of the planets were badly aspected to him at the time and place of his birth. For two minutes daily he was subjected—through the witness—to the note or notes necessary to counteract this weakness.

An Astrological Experiment

Our first experiment with this instrument was with the growth of cress. We sowed the seed in three separate pots and cast a horoscope. For Pot 1, we prescribed middle C—the note relating to the sun. Pot 2 was given B flat, the note of the planet Pluto which was badly aspected at the time of sowing the seed. Pot 3, was kept untreated and used as control. All these pots were given an equal ration of water and light. Pots 1 and 2 were given two minutes treatment daily on their respective notes.

When the cress was well grown, the appearance of the treated cress was dramatically different. Pot 1 had responded enthusiastically to middle C and its solar influence and stood straight and sturdy, whereas Pot 2, with the note of badly aspected Pluto, was very dark green, stunted and slightly bent over. Pot 3 looked quite normal but less robust than Pot 1.

We cut each lot and put them in plain envelopes marked A, B and C and sent them to a skilled radiesthetist asking for his assessment of their respective qualities. He was told nothing of the treatment or our expectations and we were greatly encouraged by his report. A, was 100 per cent in balance, had high nutritional value and was free of all virus and bacteria. B was full of virus and bacteria and was totally out of balance and we were told not to eat it at any price. C was lacking in life energy and was not entirely in balance but was edible. This was obviously a potentially powerful instrument to be used with care and discretion. Our first human patient to be treated on what came to be known as 'Ding Dong', was a chronic asthmatic and the treatment was extremely successful except that he had regular attacks every weekend, when we were both away, or when he missed his two minutes treatment.

I still have 'Ding Dong' but, alas, no longer have time to cast horoscopes so it is not in use.

One interesting result of this excursion into astrology, was in the case of a young child who was mentally defective. His birth had been premature and induced and his horoscope was such that, born where and when he was, his planets were so ill aspected that he had little chance of enjoying a normal life. Had this child been allowed to go to his full term, the pattern of his horoscope would have been substantially different and he might have led a very different life. This makes one wonder at the wisdom of the modern practice of induced births. Nature has a way of knowing best and it may be better not to coerce her for our own convenience.

Another of our special instruments comprised of one large spiral of copper wire round a core of 2½ grams of mercury in a glass tube, wrapped in thick tinfoil, enclosed in a coil of brass wire. A zinc wheel on an arm, travelled the length of the spiral, controlled by a dial on the outer casing. There was a zinc lined well set into the top in which the patient's witness was placed.

I am not sure what inspired this instrument, which was specifically for removing poisons but I imagine that its success was due to the interaction of the various metals powered by the spiral. We showed it to a sensitive who said that he could hear it humming like a hive of bees, although it had no mains connection.

We were lucky in having a friend called George Punshon, who was a skilled craftsman and built these instruments to our specifications. The measurements and materials were determined radiesthetically and had to be exact.

We created quite a sensation in a timber yard selecting the wood for this instrument by testing all their bulk timbers on the dock with our pendulums. The manager and foreman may have thought us eccentric but they ended up by trying the pendulum themselves with some success! George also designed and made his own nine dial instruments, which we still use. Many other practitioners have, no doubt, built and used their own instruments but research is time-consuming and as the practice builds and there is a growing queue of patients, they tend to come first and instrument building goes by the board.

Gem Therapy

Radionic practitioners feel free to use anything they feel may be helpful in treating their patients. I have mentioned colour and now I will come to gems.

Dr Bhattacharyya has carried out much research in India on what he calls 'gem therapy' and has written several books on this subject—*The Science of Cosmic Ray Therapy; Telepathy;* and *Gem Therapy.* He has found that just as the aspect of a planet or a musical note or a specific colour exert a specific influence on part of the human body, so do different gems. Each gem has a cosmic colour vibration. The pearl, which vibrates to cosmic orange, relates to the moon and affects the heart and the circulation of the blood. The diamond vibrates to indigo, relates to the planet Venus and affects eye, ear and nose complaints. The sapphire, on the violet cosmic ray, is good for skin conditions and nerve pain. The ruby on the red cosmic ray, relates to the sun and helps in cases of anaemia and physical debility. I have also found it helpful in promoting fertility.

Dr Bhattacharyya uses his gems in two ways, either pulverized and given orally, which was the original method, or whirled rapidly in front of a photograph of the patient. Both systems seemed successful. We use them with radionic instruments.

There is one instrument which is easily adapted to the use of gems. It is called 'Tellerek' and is of Belgian origin and consists of a copper coil wound in the shape of a narrow horseshoe. The selected gems are placed in a glass phial which spans both sides of the horseshoe and the patient's witness is placed at the open end.

It seems that there is a common denominator in all these things, colour, sound, numbers, geometry, planets and gems. They seem to be, in some way, a universal language that is understood by the formative forces which govern our lives and our well-being.

Gem therapy has been further extended by the genius of a jeweller called Gordon Prangley who has devised special instruments of healing incorporating the use of jewels of all kinds. His inspiration comes from that reservoir of knowing, the collective unconscious, and the list of cases treated by his methods cover a number of conditions deemed incurable by orthodox medicine. Further research into his discoveries might bring new hope to thousands of people suffering from supposedly incurable conditions, but research costs money and this is hard to come by if there is no profit motive behind it. You may consider this a cynical view but when I tell you that our request for funding from one source was turned down because they were 'not interested in any cure which did not involve the use of chemical substances'. Here we come to the real nub—the profit motive which has destroyed so much that is good in life today.

Radionics, which had its origin in the U.S.A., was outlawed and declared illegal by the intervention of the all-powerful drug houses. God forbid that the U.K. should fall under the same domination.

Earth is a small planet, an insignificant speck in the cosmos, and one in which things have gone terribly wrong. The root cause of all our problems seem to be simply wrong motivation.

The overriding motives of the majority of people are money and power.

Pleasure in work and even in play is measured by how much you can get for doing it, especially if you can get more than the next man. Pride in a job well done has largely gone by the board, and if you can get more for doing less—bully for you!

That the spark of humanity is still there, though dormant, is the saving grace. Faced by a common enemy a nation will unite and the motive of patriotism will take over from that of profit. Faced by a major disaster, compassion unites people of all nations. The Divine Spark suddenly becomes alive.

4. Human Case Histories

In giving case histories, we are trying to show the reader the diverse types of disease which we try and help. They have been chosen not only for their particular interest but also to give the reader an idea of the wide possibilities in radionic therapy. The following are but a few types of cases which range from osteoarthritis, asthma, and accidents, to infertility, nervous breakdowns, digestive problems, pain with unknown origin, migraines and many more.

For the last twenty years students have been trained by the School of Radionics, and have been passed by the Board of Examiners. Although they have all been trained in the same techniques, as they gain experience each one develops their own methods and approach to patients and their problems.

Records and Reports
Several practitioners keep careful monthly records of why their patients come off treatment, for example, better, improved, no better, died or 'no news'. This last may seem strange but some patients ask for help and one never hears from them again. The patient may come with great enthusiasm and the practitioner, after making a radionic analysis, commences treatment. He then writes to the patient saying that treatment has commenced and asks for regular reports. Sometimes, in spite of further letters, no word comes back.

The regularity of reports is of great importance because if there is no improvement, one wants to find out why and probably change the treatment. In the case of acute conditions, lack of news could make all the difference to the speed of recovery. The time in between reports varies according to the acuteness of the condition. This could mean every day or sometimes twice a day or, for the chronic case, once a week, once a fortnight or once a month.

These reports from patients not only supply the practitioner with information but also help build up a relationship between them. It gives the patient an opportunity to add anything about themselves which they either want to get off their chest or to mention something they forgot to put on their Case History Sheet.

Everything that is said or written between patient and practitioner is naturally confidential and because of this, help can be given in other ways than just through instruments. Many patients telephone their reports and much help can be derived from this direct link. However, practitioners do not encourage this method, except when it is genuinely helpful, since the telephone never ceases to ring and the work of making an analysis and giving treatment would be hampered.

The radionic analysis is of vital importance as it is the blueprint of the patient and must be done in a way that allows easy checking. However, emergencies do happen in accidents, sudden illness and infections. For example, with an accident, the sooner the patient is put on treatment for counteracting the effects of shock, injury bruising or haemorrhage, the better and the sooner healing takes place.

May I stress that when writing about emergencies, it is not with the idea that radionic treatment supercedes the need for orthodox medical treatment. Far from it; but patients can be helped by being given ancillary treatment, remembering that we are working through the etheric and not the physical which means that treatment is being given on two different levels and can, in many cases, be extremely beneficial.

In the following cases, which come from various practitioners, each case is headed by the condition or symptom from which patients have sought help—I have tried to give a brief background to the case followed by the practitioner's analysis and radionic treatment, ending with the result.

Antidoting Shock and Speedy Treatment

There are many forms of shock that can be helped by a trained practitioner. In any accident one of the first treatments to be given is one to antidote shock. A detailed analysis is then made to find out exactly where the damage lies. Accidents can occur in so many different ways and having put the patient on treatment to antidote shock, the actual extent of the injuries must be found. There may be just bruising but there may also be laceration, haemorrhage, internal injuries, concussion and many other factors which must be identified and treated. A correct analysis quickly made can make all the difference to the patient's recovery.

An instance of this was when a patient was riding in an event when her horse came down and rolled on her. The practitioner happened to hear of this on the radio and, as the rider was already being treated for a different condition, she got out her file and speedily, through the witness, found the location and extent of the injuries and started giving the appropriate treatment as soon as possible. Two hours later the patient's husband phoned the practitioner to say that his wife was in hospital after a bad fall and the practitioner was able to tell him exactly what the analysis had shown, that is, broken ribs, injury to the spine and other areas. He was amazed at the accuracy of the findings which were all confirmed by the X-ray and examination. This lady was riding in half the time she had been told to expect.

Another instance was in the case of a bad car accident. When the woman driver had been taken to hospital the first thing she asked the nurse to do was to ring her radionic practitioner to inform her of the accident. The practitioner realized this was an SOS and took immediate action.

It is difficult to assess the exact extent of the help given in this way but it always seems that the patients recover much faster than anticipated and that permanent damage is minimized.

Treating Fractures

We are often told that it must be impossible for radionics to treat anything like a broken leg. This is not, however, the case.

We have had very many cases of fractured bones which have responded astonishingly well to radionic treatment. This is not, of course, without the bone being set and immobilized or, where necessary, pinned, but radionics does most certainly speed up the knitting of the bone and the mending of the fracture. By increasing the flow of life energy to the injured tissue and by directing the elements needed for rebuilding that tissue, the bone union is brought about much faster than usual.

Asthma Due to Allergy

A woman patient, H-M, went to a radionic practitioner seeking help for her asthma which she had had for thirty years. At this time she was sixty-six and during the thirty years had tried many varied treatments, orthodox and otherwise—all to no effect. It did seem, however, that the condition was caused by allergy to cats.

In most cases of allergy, the cause is important yet very difficult to find, especially in those which commenced in adult life. In one case, the patient was medically tested and found to be allergic to feather pillows, bananas, mushrooms and shell fish, and life was not easy. Through radionics, the cause was discovered to be shock at the death of her son in the war. Treatment removed all traces of allergy and for the rest of her life she was able to eat what she liked and sleep on any pillow.

In another case of allergy, a huntsman suddenly found his hands were so sore with eczema that he could not hold the reins when riding his horse and was likely to lose his job. Radionic analysis showed allergy and, after much probing, that he was specifically allergic to the smell of raw meat. Everyday he had to cut up meat for the hounds, and the practitioner suggested he should cease doing this for a while and with radionic treatment his hands completely recovered and remained well.

Let us return to H-M and her asthma, as it is a strange story. The radionic analysis showed an unusual number of different types of shock—emotional, mental, nervous, physical and traumic. Also emotional, mental and physical stress.

Careful question and answer technique was vital in this case in order to get behind the cause of the shocks and stresses. It was like a detective novel as these difficult cases so often are and the patient was asked to confirm and add information.

The story that evolved was that, during the war, H-M and her husband were in the Far East with the children when it was over-run by the Japanese, and they were not able to return to England.

H-M and the children were able to escape on a boat to South Africa, though not without further trouble as Japanese aeroplanes attacked the ship. From the moment of escaping, H-M did not know whether her husband was alive or dead.

On arrival in South Africa, the children were feeling insecure from their ordeals, so a kitten was bought for them in an effort to help them. She came back to England and it was, in fact, after this that the allergy came to the fore and H-M could not be in the same room as a cat or even enter a house where a cat was living, without having a severe attack.

Even worse, she reacted when visiting a place where a cat had been, without having any prior knowledge that it had been anywhere near.

She received radionic treatment for nine months and at first received treatment on the Rae 24 Dial, Delawarr 9 Dial and Peggotty instruments. Also the Tansley Centre Therapy instrument was used when treating the base, throat and brow centres. This would help to restore balance to those centres which in turn would react on the physical body.

In spite of all this, it was not until the Rae Simulator was used that a real breakthrough in her condition occurred. The Simulator cards used, included allergy to cats hair which antidotes the allergy, oxygen at intervals to help expand the lungs and a card representing a cat's astral counterpart, affecting the patient's astral body. Finally, the card for suprarenal glands to normalize the function of the suprarenal glands was used and which we find so very important in asthmatic treatment.

The patient is a calm and very balanced person and through this has helped her own healing. At the end of the nine months treatment she could go anywhere where a cat was or had been. Not only this, she could even have a cat sitting on her knee and not a trace of asthma would appear with the chest entirely clear, not even a wheeze. Since treatment ceased for this particular ailment, H-M has required help for other things but the asthma has not returned at all.

Back Injuries

At 59, B.T. fell off a horse, wrenching an old back injury and damaging his left shoulder. The back injury meant he could not bend even to put on his shoes.

Most people would visit an osteopath or chiropractor and so would B.T. have done, except that he lived on the edge of the moors and miles away from anyone who could give him manipulation. He therefore relied entirely on radionic treatment.

Readers will have realized by now, how essential it is to always make a radionic analysis, however straightforward the case may be. One so often finds something else besides the immediately obvious complaint. This case was no exception.

No less than three injuries were discovered to his back—the 2nd cervical vertebra, the 4th lumbar vertebra and the sacroiliac joint, and strain to the erector spinae muscle.

He had a lot of engagements to fulfil at horse shows—it was therefore vital that a speedy recovery was made.

The displacement of the lumbar vertebra was treated with a Peggotty board and left on for several days to correct it. The muscle strain of the erector spinae was also counteracted on a Peggotty. The Delawarr 9 Dial was used, however, to antidote traumatic shock and eliminate nervous tension.

In this case too, the subtle anatomy could not be ignored and the Tansley Centre Therapy instrument was used to restore harmony to the base centre which is of great importance in spinal problems as it governs the spine and skeletal system. The Alta Major centre was also treated. The reason for this was its connection with the cervical vertebrae.

The homoeopathic remedy of Rhus Tox was given through the Rae Simulator, to complete the treatment. This was used for its effect on the stiffness in the small of the back. Having commenced treatment in the middle of November, it was halted by the middle of January, as there were no more symptoms or problems.

Shooting Accident

To start with, this case was an emergency but having dealt with the immediate problems, it was a question of restoring tissues and the sight.

The patient was a boy of 14 who was involved in a shooting accident which resulted in pellets entering both eyes causing severe haemorrhage.

He was rushed to hospital and an operation was immediately performed. It took four and a half hours and a pellet was removed from the right eye but it was found impossible to remove one from the left eye. This pellet had gone through the eye, luckily lodging itself in a relatively safe place. The prognosis for his future sight was bad at this stage.

At the same time, his radionic practitioner was informed and so radionic treatment was quickly available. In this instance, it was not a question of making an entire analysis to find the root cause for this was known. It was, however, essential to assess the intensity of the injuries and the parts of the eyes which were damaged.

As an accident immediate radionic treatment was vitally important; as important in its own way as the orthodox medical treatment and operation.

In such circumstances, treatment antidoting shock is automatically given on one of the available instruments before any questions are asked. The next thing was to check for haemorrhage and having received a positive answer, special anti-haemorrhage treatment was given.

The means of assessing the presence of shock and haemorrhage was through the use of the pendulum over the hair sample of the patient on the instrument and the question and answer technique.

Once the emergency treatment had been set in motion, the next thing, as mentioned previously, was to go deeper into finding the extent of injuries. It was found radionically that the optic nerve had been injured and there was contusion of the right eyeball. Furthermore, there was physical and traumic shock, physical stress and psychological confusion. The haemorrhage was found to be severe.

On the non-physical side, the shock and suddeness of the accident had damaged his aura, and affected the crown, brow and heart energy centres. The crown and brow centres are particularly involved with the eyes and nervous system and the heart centre is involved with the haemorrhage.

The area of physical injury was not wide and the treatment straightforward, continuing with the emergency treatment and adding treatment for the energy centres, eyes, optic nerves and the aura, on the Rae 24 Dial.

The next day, antidote to contusion of the right eyeball was added and for 18 days the treatment was intensive. At the end of this time, the patient had made tremendous progress and the outlook improved.

On making a radionic recheck, the possibility of a clot showed up in each eye. This was antidoted on a Peggotty instrument. Later the retina required stimulating and after three months, conjunctivitis had to be cleared.

At intervals, other treatment was given such as cleansing of the eyes, restoring sight and the elasticity of the vascular lamina.

The Rae Simulator was used with cards for symphytum, silica, euphrasia and natrum salicylicum which is especially for retinal haemorrhage. These were given over a long period of time.

At one stage it was thought that he would only have vision for light and dark or at best a blurred vision in the left eye. However, by March he was able to return to school and by July, the vision of the right eye was almost normal and the left eye had half-vision. The vision in both eyes was normal by September. The accident had happened in January of that year.

In spite of a risk of retinal detachment, he was able to take part in all school activities. One must stress that the boy's tremendous courage throughout, his calmness and his determination helped his recovery and the doctors were high in their praise for his courage and optimism.

I might add that he took and passed his Common Entrance in June when the vision of the left eye was still not good.

Migraine

Migraine is a condition from which many people suffer and is one which sometimes radionics can help. I would, however, like to give the following case not because it was successful but rather because it was not.

Mr T. sought help for very bad migraines. So bad that he spent at least four or five days of a week in a darkened room with the result that he could only work part-time and even this was difficult. After one month's treatment, the improvement was such that he was only spending two or three afternoons in a darkened room. He then came to see us and asked if we thought he would completely recover.

His response to treatment after one month was very encouraging and we could see no reason why he should not continue to improve. Our reply to his question was that we could not promise or guarantee his complete recovery but that having shown so much improvement already there seemed every chance of further improvement.

He said, did we realize that if he completely recovered it was possible that he would have to get a full time job. His wife would want to entertain more than at present and also might want to move house. At this we asked if he really wanted to get better and should we continue treatment? His answer was a positive 'yes' but from then on he not only ceased to improve but he retreated to his days in a darkened room and whatever treatment we gave (and we changed it often to try and get a breakthrough) it was like hitting a brick wall.

We will never know exactly what happened and why. It was as if his subconscious had dug its toes in and said it was much more comfortable being looked after, not working hard and not having to entertain or move house.

There are many possible reasons why he never got better but hard as we tried, we were never able to get rid of his migraine.

Catarrh

Mrs K. had very bad catarrh which had been present for some months and was causing her concern. A radionic analysis was made and the root cause was found to be strontium fall-out. Over and above this were displacement of a cervical vertebra, mental stress and pneumonia toxins. These were the main causes and it should be said here that the pneumonia toxins were effects left over from having had pneumonia some months before and was affecting the respiratory system generally, not just the lungs.

The first treatment was to remove the strontium fall-out on a nine dial instrument, followed by antidoting the pneumonia toxins. The displacement of the cervical vertebrae was treated on a Peggotty and it was suggested to her that a visit to an osteopath or chiropractor was advisable. In radionics we have often found that trouble in the cervical area coincides with sinusitis and catarrh.

The treatment also included the left eye minor chakra. This was given the rate for restoring harmony, so antidoting mental stress and nervous tension to complete the treatment. Base 44 was used for all these and in two months she was completely recovered and no signs of catarrh were left.

Before coming to have radionic treatment she had had various medical treatments and several tests for allergies had been taken but did not show any particular allergy although it had been thought at the time that this was the cause.

Leg Pains

This may sound a curious heading but it was the only symptom given by a patient who was in such severe pain at times that he could not do his job properly. He was a gardener and he mentioned that the pain was especially severe in the afternoon.

The analysis was not easy to make as the causes seemed to be of a psychosomatic nature and the only physical condition was tension of muscles and disharmonies in the pelvis and the iliosacral joints, although nothing was found to be displaced.

The psychosomatic problems appeared to be emotional stress affecting the central nervous system which was also affecting the endocrine glands. There was inflammation in the skeletal system and a psychosomatic problem affecting the solar plexus.

On the face of it, this did not look like a good analysis, but trusting the answers received through the use of the pendulum in conjunction with the instrument, treatment was found—this was a mixture of radionics, homoeopathy, and Bach remedies (such as olive, gentian or vine).

The Tansley centre therapy was used to treat the solar plexus chakra and the central nervous system with a mauve colour. The Rae 24 Dial treated the iliosacral joint and he was given some mezerum ointment which had been made on the simulator. This he had to apply to the painful area.

A month later, unhappiness was counteracted, harmony was restored to the astral body and the muscles were strengthened. The treatment was later changed to restoring co-ordination of the physical etheric body and the Bach remedy olive was given. The treatment took four months to really work and for the pain to completely disappear. It came back but to his shoulder and arm. Having given radionic treatment for this new development he was completely clear and could resume his gardening without pain.

Pain in Joints

The last case in this chapter is again one of pain. This time severe pain in wrists, knee and ankle joints. Mr B. thought he had arthritis and the only treatment he had received was heat and this had brought no relief.

As with all radionic analysis, the causes were of importance. Congestion of muscles, shock which had affected the adrenal glands, poor circulation and a psychosomatic aspect affecting the physical etheric were the main things.

Treatment was different and the 24 Dial was not used at all. The first thing to be given was Bach remedy mimulus pills which he took by mouth. The suprarenal glands were treated on the Rae Simulator which was a new approach to the use of this instrument and as a method of treating organs. This particular treatment was repeated several times. Vitamin B_6 was taken orally by Mr B. and progress was soon apparent. The simulator was also used to give the homoeopathic remedy strychinum.

For the first two months treatment was intensive and muscles required strengthening and tensions removed. Progress was, however, steady and when the treatment was stopped, Mr B. was without pain and absolutely mobile.

Dignity in Death

To keep people alive at all costs is too often considered the most important aspect of healing. This may be because it presents a challenge to the pride of medical science, which responds regardless of the wishes of the patient who knows he can never live a full life and can only exist as a cabbage; a cabbage, moreover, who must be maintained and cared for by his relatives.

We all have to die some time and there can be dignity and peace which makes the moment of leaving the body a wonderful transition, infinitely more peaceful than the violence and pain of birth.

We have found that patients who are near to dying can be helped enormously through radionic treatment. Treatment which seems to give them an inner peace and tranquillity and enables them to go without anguish.

Very many times we have been told that 'so and so went so peacefully', that 'so and so had such a lovely smile when she went' or that 'she just turned her head and passed on'.

These are just a few remarks that have come back to us, granted that they could apply to many dying people but when a nurse says that she has never seen anyone die so peacefully, it is food for thought.

Radionics can help not only at death but in the period leading up to it when the patient is very seriously ill, probably in pain and psychologically distressed. Through the use of the many instruments at our disposal it is possible to relieve pain and to bring calm, courage and confidence to the patient who will very often look at his illness in a totally different light without bitterness or fear.

Winning a few more years of restricted life for a patient is not the aim of radionics. The alleviation of suffering both mental and physical is, we feel, a more worthwhile objective.

Tricks and Attacks on Radionics

In common with all pioneer movements, radionics and those practising it, have been subjected to persecution, attacks and trickery in an attempt to discredit it.

There are always those who will go to elaborate and underhand methods to mock things they do not understand and do not wish to accept. This has always been so but these methods have never succeeded in stifling a worthwhile discovery.

Scepticism is quite understandable but outright comdemnation, without having first taken the trouble to investigate the object of attack, is foolish.

There are those whose mission in life seems to be to attack what they do not understand and do not wish to accept. Among these is a medical journalist who delights in attempting to catch out the unwary radionic practitioner. Writing under an assumed name, this gentleman wrote to a practitioner enclosing a snip of cat's hair and a phoney case history, giving details of symptoms which anyone with any medical knowledge would recognize as those of diabetes. The practitioner, acting in good faith, made an analysis which indicated that the patient was suffering from disturbances in the digestive and nervous systems. That this was an accurate analysis was confirmed by the doctor as he admitted that his cat was suffering from worms and had been 'a bit neurotic'. Far from being impressed by this, the doctor castigated the practitioner for not diagnosing diabetes from the given symptoms. This simply shows how little the doctor knows about radionics. A radionic analysis is aimed at discovering the underlying causes of the patient's problems, not to jump to conclusions from given symptoms which can result in the wrong—and sometimes fatal—treatment.

Had the practitioner said that the patient was a diabetic, it would have been totally wrong and the doctor would have been justified in his criticism. As it was, the practitioner came out of the exercise with a good deal more credit than the doctor.

A number of other attempts have been made to trick practitioners. When bloodspots were used as witnesses, instead of hair, it was even easier and the blood of birds and a variety of beasts were used to lure the practitioner into error and expose him to mockery.

Both Ruth Drown and others were subjected to this form of attack and in the United States, where the assault was at its most savage, phoney patients wearing hidden tape recorders on their person, related imaginary ills in order to confound Ruth Drown and condemn her by her own voice.

One joker sent a spot of pheasant's blood to Mabel Lloyd with a trumped up case history; but there he met his match. Mabel Lloyd was a very shrewd and intuitive old lady and she was not fooled. Her diagnosis was that, if the patient had flown higher, he would not have been hurt!

This mindless attack, apart from being an irretrievable waste of time and energy, does nothing to enhance the cause of the critic or to halt the progress of radionics. Practitioners may suffer, as Ruth Drown did, through her practice being shut down and her health destroyed. The de la Warrs suffered heavy financial burdens in successfully defending their good name but the work initiated by Albert Abrams goes from strength to strength and the seed of truth that lay in his discovery will continue to grow no matter how many snares are laid in its path.

5. Animal Case Histories

The treatment of animals by a radionic practitioner or, indeed, by anyone other than a qualified veterinary surgeon, was illegal. It is still against the law to diagnose and give advice on the treatment of animals under the Veterinary Surgeons Act 1966.

It seems strange that it should be quite in order to practise factory farming and that the appalling cruelty of vivisection should be upheld by law, whereas healing an animal by unorthodox means is not only frowned upon by authority but may be punished by a heavy fine. Even trained veterinary surgeons run the risk of severe displeasure by the Royal Veterinary College if they are caught using radionics in their practice. This is sad because radionic practitioners could do so much to help them in the diagnosis of animal complaints. An animal is at greater disadvantage than a human when he is ill as he cannot describe how he feels or what led up to his illness and much of the veterinary diagnosis must, of necessity, be guesswork.

All animals have etheric bodies and energy centres but they do not have the higher bodies of man. They are analysed and treated in the same way as human beings and the first principle is to discover the root cause of their disability. Animals of all kinds respond well to radionic treatment and the incidence of successful treatment is markedly higher than with humans, probably because they offer no subconscious resistance to treatment and have the genuine desire to recover. There are, happily, a number of radionic practitioners who love animals and are prepared to risk the law and to treat them along with their human patients. I am going to describe a few cases to show how well justified they are in their action.

The Insights of Radionic Analysis
I will take first, two cases of young horses whose owners had been advised to have them put down.

The first was a 14 hand gelding, 20 months old who reared up and fell over backwards when playing with other ponies in a field. Soon after this he developed a peculiarity of gait which grew steadily worse. There was a lack of control in his back legs and he trotted at an angle instead of in a straight line. He was examined by two vets, both of whom said that he was a 'wobbler' and should be put down as there was no known cure for this condition.

A radionic analysis was made on this gelding on November 13th and showed a displacement of the sixth lumbar vertebra and a lack of co-ordination between the astral and etheric bodies.

Treatment was given to correct the displacement of the lumbar vertebra on the Peggotty instrument, the meninges of the spinal cord and the lumbar nerves were normalized on the Rae Base 44 instrument, the astral and etheric bodies were treated for co-ordination and the energy centre at the base of the brain was normalized, also on Base 44. A letter from the owner said that steady improvement was noted as soon as treatment started and by January 4th, it was only occasionally that he did not seem one hundred per cent sound. He is now fully recovered.

Another so-called 'wobbler' was a two year old thoroughbred colt who was said by three vets to be 'suffering from an incurable disease'. They all agreed that he should be put down at once, as there was no future for him. The pattern of the analysis had much in common with the other case. Lack of co-ordination in the astral and etheric bodies and displacement in the vertebrae; this time the axis and the fourteenth thoracic vertebra. The vagus and the lumbar nerves and the medulla oblongata in the hind brain were normalized on the Base 44 instrument and, once again, the energy centre at the base of the brain. The owner was asked to call in a horse osteopath to correct the displacements manually.

The osteopath confirmed the displacements and did his best to correct them but was gloomy about the outcome of the case but the owner remained optimistic, in spite of all adverse opinions and radionic treatment was continued. Two months later, the osteopath called again to see the colt and said he could hardly believe his eyes; it had improved so much that he would not have recognized it as the same animal. He found three vertebrae slightly out of place which he corrected and the colt is now standing at a stud in Italy and thought to have a great future as a stallion.

The fact that emerges from these two cases is that symptoms are often deceptive and that owing to lack of communication with animals, conclusions reached are not always correct. Radionic analysis, being carried out on a different level, may get nearer the truth.

Some More Cases of Displacement

Another interesting horse case was a thoroughbred yearling colt which had been discarded by his owner as he was born with a deformed fore-foot which turned in and prevented proper action.

Analysis showed injury and displacement of the fetlock joint at birth and treatment was commenced towards the end of November. This displacement was treated on a Peggotty instrument; the energy centres of the coronet, the part of the brain that controls the leg area, the ligaments in the fetlock and the thyroid gland, were treated on Base 44.

In mid December, further treatment was given on Base 44 to eliminate concretions in the phalanx bones and to manifest optimal harmony in the joint. The energy centres in the coronet were also treated again. The fore-foot gradually straightened out and the horse is now in full use.

It would, of course, have been very much quicker had the case been treated before the joint became set at the wrong angle but even so, it is remarkable what can be done in a comparatively short space of time.

Another case of displacement was in a miniature schnauzer, aged 18 months. This was a bitch with a thrown shoulder and she was limping and in pain.

Analysis showed displacement of the shoulder joint and congestion in the ulna and in the muscular tissues. Treatment was given on Peggotty to reduce the displacement; the ulna and the muscular tissue were treated three times on Base 44 and, after twelve days, the owner reported great improvement and hardly any limp. Three weeks later, no lameness at all was apparent but there was still a little stiffness in the morning and slight tenderness. One month later, the bitch was one hundred per cent normal.

Quite a different kind of case was a Great Dane dog, nine years old who had been ill for six weeks. He had no appetite and his stool was very loose. He was very thin and weak and had great difficulty in eating owing to a profuse flow of saliva. He had been having liver injections and it was suggested that he should be put down as the kidneys might be affected, putting more strain on his heart.

It was at this unpromising stage that a radionic analysis was carried out. This showed a high degree of poison in the bloodstream, a catalyst deficiency in the tissues which also had toxins and congestion and, finally, congestion of the spleen.

Treatment was given to eliminate poison on Peggotty and also on Base 44 repeated three times. Elimination of toxins was repeated three times on Base 44.

The thyroid gland was normalized in two treatments and the spleen and the sublingual glands were treated on Base 44. This dog started to improve after one week's treatment but he was not eating very much. Three weeks later the excess flow of saliva had stopped and he was eating better and getting stronger. The stools had improved. After five weeks, he was keen on his food and his walks and was back to full health. A year and a half later, the practitioner received a letter from the owner to say that the dog's back legs were paralyzed and, owing to his size, this was presenting serious problems. A new analysis was made which showed a displacement in his sacrum. His witness was placed on a Peggotty for one month, set for 'displacement of sacrum'. After the first week, he could get up and stand with help and became stronger and more confident every day and by the end of the month, when he came off treatment, he was again going for walks and getting into the car unaided.

The lives of three out of the four last animals would have been forfeited had it not been for radionics, so it is hardly surprising that both owners and practitioners think it a worthwhile proposition in spite of the disapproval of the law.

Some Further Examples

A 12-year-old pony with a history of laminitis for all six years in his present ownership, came in for treatment in mid March as he was said to have ringbone as well as laminitis and there were doubts as to whether he would be fit for the child to ride him in the summer holidays. Analysis showed the parathyroid glands to be out of balance and the tissues to be inflamed.

The condition of ringbone was put up on Peggotty and treatment was given on this every other day. On Base 44, the energy centres of the coronets were given one treatment. The parathyroid glands, the sensitive laminae in the feet, the lymph and the plasma cells of the blood were all normalized.

The pony came off treatment on 3 May, perfectly sound and a letter was received from his owner in December saying that the pony had grown new feet with no trace of either laminitis or ringbone in them. He was sound as a bell, very happy and seemed ten years younger. It was not only the pony that was happy, the owner, the child and the practitioner all rejoiced!

Quite a different case was a nine year old thoroughbred gelding who had been coughing for six weeks. Coughs, as you may know, are very unpopular in racing stables, and the trainer had tried one cough medicine after the other without the slightest effect. He told me that the horse appeared to have something stuck in his throat. When he coughed, he put his head down, stuck out his neck and stamped his foot. My analysis showed the cause to be one hundred per cent psychosomatic. This is unusual in animals but this horse must have thought he had had a poor deal because one treatment of 'anti-self pity' on Base 44 cleared up the trouble and stopped the cough!

Some cases treated at the Cotswold Wildlife Park included a Da Brazza monkey, an 18-month-old female which had a terribly poisoned leg due, it was thought, to a bite from a merecat in the next door cage. She had been injected with multi-vitamin and penicillin and terramycin and had become increasingly moribund and was thought to be dying of septicaemia.

Treatment was started on 14 January. Poison was antidoted on the Rae Simulator and on Peggotty and homoeopathic gunpowder was projected also on the Simulator. Anti-traumic shock was given on Base 44 and the blood and the lymph glands were normalized.

Three days later, lachesis muta was given on the Simulator and an improvement was noted. By the 25th, the inflammation round the wound had gone and it appeared clean and treatment was given to heal the skin both on Base 44 and Base 10. This little monkey made a perfect recovery and came off treatment at the beginning of April.

At the same time, a two year old Eland Bull in the same park came under treatment. The symptoms were emaciation and listlessness, symptomatic of 'pine'. The veterinary treatment given was the same as for the monkey; multi-vitamin, penicillin and paracure worm powder and he was making no improvement. Radionic analysis showed the pancreas and the spleen to be out of balance and there was a pronounced cobalt deficiency and diabetes.

Diabetes and the diabetic factor were eliminated on the Simulator and Peggotty and cobalt was given on a nine dial instrument. The Islands of Langerhans were normalized on Base 44.

The basic cause of the cobalt deficiency was not faulty diet but a heavy infestation of worms in the gut. Internal parasites are voracious eaters of cobalt and this element is essential for the production of beneficial bacteria in the digestive tract, in order to synthesize Vitamin B_{12}. If it is all gobbled up by the parasites the animal suffers a Vitamin B_{12} deficiency. This Eland made a complete recovery.

One of the lions in the film *Born Free* was badly injured in an unfortunate encounter with a buffalo after he had been rehabilitated in the game reserve in East Africa. This lion was found lying out in the bush, immobilized with a broken shoulder, unable to hunt and, therefore, unable to eat. Toni Harthoorn and his wife Sue, both highly qualified vets, were called to the rescue and flew out from Nairobi to perform an operation which saved the lion's life. At the same time, some hair from his mane was sent back to the U.K. and put on radionic treatment to heal the bone and the torn muscles and ligaments. The advantages of long range treatment are infinite and radionic practitioners keep the witness of all their patients so that, in the event of an emergency, they may be put on treatment at a moment's notice, no matter where they may be at the time.

In this plastic age, children and animals are open to hazards which did not exist in the time of their grandparents. Children play with plastic bags and if they put them over their heads, they are apt to be suffocated. The careless picnicker may leave the plastic bags which have contained his sandwiches, lying on the grass and cattle may eat them and harm their complicated stomach arrangements. Another aspect of the harm that plastics can do is illustrated in the following case history of a horse which was losing condition and weight rapidly. It was eating well but drinking very little and was increasingly lethargic. Radionic analysis showed that an unidentified poison was present in the liver, spleen, pancreas and blood. Further investigation showed the origin of the poison to come from plastic and the owner was asked if he could throw some light on possible sources. It transpired that the horse's food was stored in a plastic bag, it was fed out of a plastic bowl and the drinking water was in a black plastic bucket. All these containers were put under scrutiny by questioning with the pendulum and the black bucket appeared to be the worst offender. The owner was asked to withdraw all plastic containers and this was done. Treatment was given on Base 44 to eliminate the poison and to normalize the liver, spleen, pancreas and blood.

The horse started to drink more water immediately and within a few days there was a marked improvement in condition but it took six weeks of treatment to get all the organs working normally.

This is not an isolated case, other horses and some goats have been found to have suffered from drinking out of these buckets which are only meant for heavy duty and rough work and are made from waste plastic.

I would like to add one rather horrifying proof of the power of the mind when used for the wrong purpose.

I have had three different patients from the ranks of top show ponies all being affected in the same way. Pulled in at the top of their class, all goes well until the final canter then, without exception, these perfectly schooled ponies go beserk and for no apparent reason become completely unruly. They are then, naturally enough, moved down the line and another pony wins the class. On one such occasion the pony concerned had a weal across its back as though it had been struck savagely with a whip. Nothing had touched it, but if proof is required of the effect of thought on physical substance here it is, and it is sad that one who has so much power that could be turned to good purpose prefers to fritter it away on personal ambitions. Such a one will have much to answer and will inevitably pay the price in the long run.

Group Treatment

One of the more fascinating features of radionic treatment is the fact that a whole group of animals such as a herd of cows or a flock of chickens, can be treated from the witness of one of their number. This is particularly useful when preventive treatment is being given against such things as contagious abortion or mastitis.

This is fairly logical as such herds and flocks seem to be controlled by one mind or group spirit but it does not stop there. Consider the case of the crossbred Irish Terrior puppy in the kennel for unwanted dogs; the owner of the kennel sought radionic treatment for this pup which was suffering from a skin disorder which had taken all the hair off his rear end. From the front he looked like an adorable teddy bear but, of course, nobody wanted him when he turned round.

All previous methods of treatment had been unsuccessful but castor oil was being applied to keep the skin supple. Radionic analysis revealed that the trouble was caused by microscopic parasites in the skin. These parasites were the type which could not be washed off so radionic treatment was given on Base 44, to eliminate the parasites and to normalize the skin, the hair and the blood. The owner was recommended to continue applying the castor oil. After two months treatment, the bald patches were well covered by a growth of new hair. This was all that the owner had hoped for but what he had not expected was that, an old dog in the next kennel, only separated by wire, had, apparently, received the same treatment although not through any witness or design, and that the troublesome skin complaint from which he had been suffering and which had resisted all treatment had also been completely cured.

An example of intentional group treatment is demonstrated in the following case. When cattle are brought in from the fields for fattening in yards, they are usually dosed for worms and internal parasites. One particular farmer was producing organic beef and did not want to use the usual medicaments. As it was intended that some of the cattle would be sold and others purchased it was not practicable to use hair specimens as a witness. Photographs of the yards were therefore used for this purpose.

Treatment was given on Base 44 both to eliminate all internal and external parasites and to protect the cattle from further infestations of parasites. Garlic was also projected on a nine dial instrument. This is not only an excellent remedy for worm infestations but is also a sovereign remedy for infections of all kinds.

In the days before sprays and weed killers, our hedgerows were a natural medicine chest from which our animals could help themselves. Now they are deprived of this and are dosed with antibiotics and hormones. When these cattle went for slaughter, the butchers found them to be completely free from worms and internal parasites which was unusual enough to cause comment.

Here is another case of mass treatment, this time a flock of hens kept in deep litter. The eggs from this flock were being sold to a hatchery and it was most important that the shells of the egss should be strong and perfect. So when the hens sickened and started to produce eggs with soft shells, the farmer asked for a radionic analysis. Eggs and feathers were used as witness and analysis showed that the hens were not assimilating the calcium in their ration as, by an error of the supplier, Vitamin D was missing from the food.

These hens were immediately given the rate for Vitamin D_2 on a nine dial instrument until the food had been changed. They were also given a rate specially made for them on Base 44 as an initial boost. Within a fortnight, everything was back to normal. The suppliers replaced the poultry meal free of charge.

Another sort of bird also benefited from radionics. This was a seven year old canary which developed stiff and swollen feet and legs so that it could not perch. It was eating very little and looked very miserable. A small feather was sent as witness and on completion of the analysis, rheumatism and a chill were found to be the basic cause of this little bird's trouble.

As there are no special rates for canaries in the ratebook, special rates were made for this particular bird and he was treated on Base 44 for a period of two months after which time it could again perch and behave normally. It lived happily for over two years longer and then died suddenly when it was almost ten years old.

Conclusion

We are often puzzled to know why some animal patients respond almost instantaneously to radionic treatment while others are slow in showing any reaction. I have known a case where the character and behaviour of a thoroughbred filly was completely changed almost overnight by a treatment to eliminate ovarian cysts. It had been impossible to pick up her back feet without being savagely kicked and she was bad tempered, uneasy and rampaged round her box every night scraping up all her bedding. After two days treatment she was as quiet as a lamb and her owner could pick up all her feet without fear of being savaged. She also slept quietly at night without disturbing her bedding.

It is a never ending source of wonder to me and although I have been working in this field continuously for twenty-five years, I am still astonished at these minor miracles.

N.B. The Royal Veterinary College has now lifted its ban on the *treatment* of animals by radionic practitioners, but analysis of conditions and advice to owners is still outside the law. It is a measure of current lack of understanding that the College concludes that treatment could be given without finding the cause of the problem. One suspects that it is only because it is deemed impossible to affect an animal at a distance that it is now permissible to do so.

6. Radionics in Agriculture

The use of radionics in agriculture and horticulture has been slow to develop in the U.K. but a start has been made and there is obviously a great future for it.

This work was pioneered in the U.S.A. many years ago by Curtis Upton, who was fired with enthusiasm by the work of Albert Abrams and determined to apply it to the diagnosis and treatment of the disease of plants and crops.

Early Achievements

He adapted Abrams' instruments and carried out the diagnosis from a leaf or a photographic negative of a plot of land placed in the instrument as witness. He was successful at ridding crops of unwelcome infestations by adding a small quantity of a reagent to the witness on the instrument which was obnoxious to the insect plaguing the crop. This worked well from a distance and aphis, beetles and worms either died or left the crop.

Upton did not stop at protecting crops from infestations of all kinds. He researched also into the improvement of quality and yield and an increase of thirty per cent was actually achieved in one crop of potatoes. Readers may wonder how it was, in the light of these obvious successes where pests were controlled without the use of poisonous sprays and crops were increased without the application of expensive fertilizers, that radionic agriculture did not take the farming world by storm. Without being too cynical, I would suggest that a great deal of money is tied up in both agricultural sprays and fertilizers and that empirical proof is not always acceptable, even to the scientific mind. Just as Abrams' work in the medical field was examined by 'experts' and dismissed as unscientific, so were Upton's successful projects examined by senior scientists who thought fit not to publish a report on them and swept their findings neatly under the carpet to the satisfaction of suppliers of agricultural chemicals throughout the United States.

In these days of growing world population, with the constant threat of hunger in the developing countries; of the increasing menace of pollution stemming from the use of poisons in controlling pests, it seems crazy not to encourage a method of growing more food with higher nutritional value at vastly less expense and without any risk of increasing the pollution problem. Man truly is his own worst enemy in a situation like this and in what purports to be a democracy, it is up to the people to express their opinion. Are they willing to continue high risk agriculture for the sake of high profit agriculture suppliers or are they in favour of research into practical methods of food production by natural means co-operating with nature rather than coercing her?

Enid Eden, one time head of training in the Radionic School, has been treating farm lands, market gardens and stock and instructing other practitioners in the art of agricultural and horticultural radionics. Here are a few of her cases:

Oil Seed Rape
This crop is particularly vulnerable to attack by pollen beetle and seed weevil and the aim of treatment was to prevent any such attack by instrumental means and not to resort to spraying unless it became absolutely necessary.

A map was used as witness and placed on a Base 10 instrument and special treatment rates were made with the dual purpose of making the rape unpalatable to the pests and to encourage the predators of these creatures. In fact, co-operating with natural controls already employed by nature.

This treatment was given daily and at the same time, a check was made to see whether a colour should be added to any rate. It was found that this varied throughout the spectrum except for yellow, which was never used. Sometimes no colour was required.

The crop was inspected at regular intervals and although the dandelions and hedge mustard round the field and on the roadside verge were covered with both pollen beetle and seed weevil, those on the crop were well below the level at which it would become necessary to bring in the spray. The treatment was, therefore, proved successful.

Protection Against Mildew

Another case on the same farm was in preventing mildew from attacking half a field of home-grown barley.

This field was divided in half so that a close study could be made of the efficacy of agricultural radionics and a comparison made between radionic and orthodox treatment. The orthodox half of the field was dressed with Milstem (the usual dressing against mildew). The other half had no dressing but relied on radionics to protect it. A map of the field and a sample of barley were used as witnesses. The rates used were for antidoting mildew and for making the crop resistant to mildew. Sometimes a medium blue colour was added and sometimes a rate for poppy.

This treatment was given on a nine dial instrument and was repeated throughout the growing season. At the time, when mildew would normally be expected, the field was inspected by an expert who suggested that on the half that had been planted with dressed seed, spraying was advisable but on the half radionically treated, it was unnecessary.

Again a triumph for natural science and economy for the farmer.

Soil Acidity

Horticultural cases are also of interest and show the wide range of radionic application.

A grower arrived one Easter, with bags of soil and boxes of little lettuces, most of which had been planted in greenhouses. The lower leaves of the plants were yellow and dying.

The grower had carried out his usual pH test on the soil and found that it was too acid (pH value 5.5). Calcium was needed but could not be applied.

Two witnesses were used for analysis—a lettuce leaf and a small sample of soil. The analysis confirmed that the plants lacked calcium but also an unnamed trace element which was identified by calling it TE3. It was also discovered that only the soil needed treatment after the initial treatment to the plants of calcium and a deep blue colour on a nine dial instrument.

A special rate was made for TE3 and the soil was treated with this and with the rate for calcium daily on the same instrument until the lettuce was harvested.

It is interesting to note that after two weeks of treatment, the pH value of the soil became 7.0. There was a very high percentage of top quality lettuce in the 1,200 dozen which were marketed.

Assisting Development

Another case which shows the versatility of radionics is demonstrated in the tomato mystery. These plants were being grown commercially in pots for sale. Some were in red clay pots and others in plastic pots.

Those in the clay pots looked dark green and vigorous. Those in the plastic pots were similar in size but were a very pale green and therefore looked very sickly.

Two plants (in pots) were brought, one of each sort, to use as witnesses.

The analysis of the plant in the plastic pot showed it to be suffering from poor circulation of air in the soil and that it lacked iron.

It was recommended that an iron supplement should be given to these plants as they were for sale the next week. This was done and they recovered in a few days. No radionic treatment was given.

Analysing the plant in the clay pot, it was interesting to discover that it was able to get the minute quantity of iron that it required from the clay pot and that the air could circulate through the clay, whereas it could not do so through the plastic.

Enid was faced by a different problem when she was asked, on 7 December, to treat Azalea plants being grown in three greenhouses, hopefully for the Christmas market.

The buds of these plants had not developed sufficiently and it was apparent that they were going to be at least one week late in coming to hand and would therefore miss the market altogether. A diagram of the greenhouses, containing 6,000 plants, and a few Azalea leaves from each of the houses, were used as witnesses.

Special rates were made 'to assist the development of bud' at the same time using different colours starting with deep purple, then a mid green and finally, a rose pink.

Treatment was given on a Base 44 instrument and on 15 December Enid was told by the grower that the buds were developing well and it looked as though all would be sold by 23 December. The control plants which were not treated were still not going to be ready for sale by Christmas.

It will be seen from these cases that both the approach and the treatment are quite different from that of Curtis Upton. An approach of persuasion more than attack; perhaps more subtle than Upton's frontal assault on pests but nonetheless effective.

Ripening Tomatoes

Now we have another variant which has also met with success. The problem here was in ripening tomatoes planted out of doors on the Isle of Mull which, all things being equal, should not be possible.

The variety grown was 'Outdoor Girl' and they were sown at the end of February in seeding compost and transplanted in three stages of growth up to 9" pots. Radionic treatment was started at the end of May when the plants were transplanted into their permanent site, chosen for its shelter and facing south.

Treatment was given on Base 44 and was exclusively rated for the energy patterns of stars, constellations and signs of the zodiac.

A good number of ripe red tomatoes were harvested by September when a gale took its toll. The condition of the top soil and the sub-soil at the end of the experiment was interesting. The top soil had deteriorated, the sub-soil on the other hand showed a marked improvement.

What, then, can be learned from these diverse experiments in aiding natural growth? Firstly that it is a valid and economical proposition. Secondly that there is more than one way in which it can be done. There are probably many other ways which have not yet been tried out but the main principle remains the same, the harnessing of natural forces by devious means of application.

Laboratory Experiments

The Delawarr Laboratories carried out a series of experiments in 1956. The first method used was by treating vermiculite on a nine dial standard instrument set 'to increase the crop'. Twelve standard 7" flower pots were filled from a common source and planted with nine seeds of spring oats. The seeds were planted in holes 1½" deep. In six pots, the holes were filled with treated vermiculite and the other six were untreated and grown as controls.

All twelve pots were kept under careful observation. The dates of germination were noted and although the seeds in the treated pots were slower to germinate than those in untreated soil, they caught up and ended at exactly the same number as those in the untreated pots. At intervals, seeds were removed from one treated and one untreated pot and the plants were measured and weighed and photographed and the average height and weight of those from the treated pots was significantly greater than those from the untreated pots. This experiment was continued after harvesting the treated and the untreated seeds to test the relevant fertility of both lots. The average germination of the untreated samples was 62.4% against 95.7% in the treated samples and the increase of weight of thrashed seed of treated over untreated was 241%, the increase of panicles was 219%; and the weight of straw was 100% more than in the controls. Quite an impressive result but obviously presenting problems in large-scale application.

Other experiments were carried out at the laboratories both with treated vermiculite and with direct radiation from elements set to make minerals in the soil available and to change acid soil to alkaline but these were not pursued on a large scale.

Natural Farming

Work on a wider concept was carried out by a farmer called Bill Kent. He was a remarkable man with profound faith and great sincerity. A skillful radiesthetist, he used his pendulum in all his work and it served him well.

He bought a farm in Gloucestershire which was in such poor heart that his friends all advised him against it and told him that he would never make anything of it. Undeterred, he embarked on a programme of organic farming in which not one ounce of artificial fertilizers or pesticides was used on his land. Every field was tested for suitability for its purpose. Parts of it were drained and reclaimed for the growing of crops. All seed was treated radionically before being sown and the land itself was treated on a special radionic instrument. The first principle was to ensure the circulation of air and water throughout the soil and he was always looking for balance and harmony. He had visions of rates for spiritual qualities which he applied to the land as well as enzymes, minerals and the helpful bacteria. He used to tell us that these rates appeared before his eyes as he meditated and by question and answer with his pendulum, he would gradually discover their meaning.

Bill did a great deal of painstaking research on the beneficial assets of different kinds of seaweed. These were collected from all over the world and mixed in exact proportions to make a liquid which he called K9. A very small amount of this, diluted in water, was sprayed over his crops to increase growth and quality. Indeed quality was the key note of all his work and he was less interested in the appearances of his crops than in its nutritional value.

This seems to me to be a completely valid outlook which is too much neglected in modern agriculture. A fat, lush crop boosted by artificial fertilizers will command a high price quite regardless of its nutritional content. Vegetables, trimmed and washed and packaged in cellophane will sell in the supermarkets even if they taste of nothing. Bill's quest for true value was justified in a feeding experiment which was conducted for two years and observed and monitored by Bristol University.

He brought in a bunch of store cattle which were divided into two equal groups. One group was fed exclusively on food grown on the farm, the other had exactly similar food bought in from elsewhere.

All the food was weighed as it was fed and when the beasts went to market, it was recorded that those fed on his own produced food had consumed only two-thirds of the amount consumed by the control group but, in spite of this, were superior both in weight and in quality. They had been notably more happy and contented and the high nutritional value of the home-grown food had paid off.

The experiment was repeated under similar conditions with the same result. Bill really loved the land and on many occasions he drove us round it in his Land Rover and told us of all his successes and mistakes and showed us a specially blessed piece of pasture where he would put any ailing beast in the certain knowledge that it would make a rapid recovery.

When Bill became too crippled with arthritis to continue farming, he sold a farm that was unrecognizable as the one he had bought. Bill Kent was a great man, slow in speech but profound in knowledge and we all miss him and his wisdom now that he has gone.

Conclusion

In conclusion, I hope that I have presented an overall picture of the growth and development of radionics and made some contribution towards an understanding of the theory and scope of this therapy. It is only one of many methods of healing the sick and it is not claimed that it is the answer to all ills, either for man or beast. It is, however, a proven method, it has succeeded where orthodox methods have failed and also has no damaging side effects. The worst it can do is to do no good.

It is also a method which is in line with the thinking of the New Age. As man evolves away from the age of materialism and begins to see himself as a spiritual being as well as a creature of flesh and blood, we begin to understand the true scope of the mind. The level of consciousness which permeates all matter will respond to instructions, whether these be mental (via the unconscious mind, working through the autonomic nervous system) or through coded instructions to cell structures of the mental spheres of the patient.

Self-Healing
The capacity of the body to heal itself is infinite. All the machinery is there to rush the leucocytes of the blood to the seat of an injury or infection. The endocrine glands are poised for the signal to manufacture and pour out secretions and hormones to deal with any emergency. However, the system sometimes falls down when blockages occur and the message fails to get through. Radionic treatment will clear the blockages if properly directed so that the message is received and understood. In the end it is always the patient who heals himself. The Life Energy, thought by Ruth Drown to be the true healer, will cope with any situation if given a clear

run. The role of radionics is to aid and encourage the natural processes of man and beast in accordance with the divine plan. The mechanics of living are such that they can adapt even to the unnatural and abused way of modern life—even when undermined by stress, hypertension and wrong diet. Yet, as has been said, this is only possible if the channels of life energy are kept clear. This may sound simpler than, in fact, it is. A very clear and objective mind is essential in making an analysis.

The deep causes which lie behind a blockage must be accurately identified. It is no good clearing a blockage without removing the cause or the problem will only recur. The mental processes of the patient are subtle and obscure and the command 'know thyself' is surely one of the most difficult of all to obey. Man is an enigma to himself, except on the lowest level and this is not what counts in the long run.

New cults and methods of healing are springing up all over the world. All have their histories of success and failure. The reason behind success and failure is still obscure. Some patients respond and others do not but natural therapies, though they may not always save life, do not have the trail of illness which is sometimes the side-effects of drug therapy.

The Goal of Natural Therapy

The passionate drive of doctors to preserve life at all costs is absent in natural therapy. It is, after all, natural to die. The unnatural methods adopted by orthodox medicine to circumvent this process often results in utter misery both to patient and relations. The dignity of death is precluded and replaced by drips, tubes, injections and drugs; all to no good purpose. The real man, on higher levels, is completely ignored and discounted as irrelevant and yet it is this, the higher spiritual man, which is most important; in all holistic healing, it is the spiritual part of man which has priority. The effects on the material body are secondary. It is our practice in cases of terminal illness, to put the patient on spiritual light into the pineal gland and it is fascinating to record that, although most patients will then pass on peacefully, and without stress, others will make a complete and unexpected recovery without any other form of treatment.

Much has yet to be done in the field of preventive medicine which would lift a heavy burden from the overloaded National Health

Service and prevent the massive loss of man-hours in industry. One of the great advantages of radionic analysis is the early detection of serious conditions which are relatively simple to eradicate before they develop.

The monumental sums spent on drugs, sprays and artificial fertilizers could certainly be cut dramatically by the adoption of natural methods applied to both health and agriculture.

If complete harmony with nature is attained, health and happiness are a natural corollary. This is true for man, beast and all living things, including the soil and all that grows in it. Too high a goal? Maybe, but unless we aim at the stars, we will achieve less than we are able and as we go on working and learning as we work, so we are making slow progress towards our objective.

Further Reading

Bhattacharyya, Bentoytosh: *Gem Therapy* (Calcutta).
—— *The Science of Cosmic Ray Therapy* (Calcutta).
—— *Telepathy* (Calcutta).
Collins, Rodney: *Theory of Celestial Harmony* (Vincent Stuart).
Tansley, David: *Dimensions of Radionics* (Health Science Press).
—— *Radionics and the Subtle Anatomy of Man* (Health Science Press).
Briggs, John P. and Peat, F. David: *Looking Glass Universe* (Fontana).
Mason, Keith: *Radionics and Progressive Energies* (The C. W. Daniel Co. Ltd.).

Index